"Are you all right?"

Alex felt his way to the edge of the bed and sat down.

"I'm just tired." She kissed his hand as he brushed a strand of hair off her cheek. "It hit me all of a sudden."

He reached to turn on the lamp, but Larkin stopped him.

"Are you sure our walk down memory lane isn't what put you to sleep?"

She was quiet for a moment; then she said, "I saw a picture of Rikki in Phil and Judy's bedroom. She was beautiful."

His throat tightened. "Yes, she was."

"You must miss her terribly."

"I did for a long time," he said. "Now I miss what could have been more than what once was." Having Larkin by his side made all the difference. That hard shell of loneliness didn't stand a chance against her warmth and generosity.

With love:
To Sunny and George—for Joanthony's,
The Candy Man and so much more,
and
to Sally—for high-energy pep talks,
Disney World and hurricane warnings,
Miami-style. You are missed.

Other novels by Barbara Bretton

Silhouette Sensation

Second Harmony
Nobody's Baby
Mrs. Scrooge
Bundle of Joy

Promises in the Night

BARBARA BRETTON

SILHOUETTE

Sensation

All the characters in this book have no existence outside the imagination of the Author, and have no relation whatsoever to anyone bearing the same name or names. They are not even distantly inspired by any individual known or unknown to the Author, and all the incidents are pure invention.

*First published in Great Britain in 1994
by Silhouette Books, Eton House, 18-24 Paradise Road,
Richmond, Surrey TW9 1SR*

© Barbara Bretton 1986

Silhouette, Silhouette Sensation and Colophon are
Trade Marks of Harlequin Enterprises B.V.

ISBN 0 373 59342 2

18-9411

Made and printed in Great Britain

Chapter One

Stop.

Take a deep breath.

Try again.

Larkin Walker inhaled slowly, then straightened the index cards that held key words from her speech in bold black letters. Course 36, "Organization: Key to Success," recommended using these makeshift cue cards, but Larkin was beginning to think that method worked only for speakers whose hands didn't shake like a clothesline in a stiff north wind.

"Learning needn't stop when... Who says you're too old to learn to play the piano or take up ballet? It's only a matter of—oh, no!"

Index cards cascaded to the floor, sliding under chairs and slipping beneath the water cooler in the corner of the room, where other workshop speakers sat clustered together. Larkin stooped down quickly, praying that she could gather up her notes before anyone noticed.

No such luck.

"Don't tell me you have stage fright!" Adele, owner of the School for Advancement, gave Larkin a look from beneath her individually applied false eyelashes. "I can hardly believe you'd find that little group in the auditorium terrifying."

"Speaking before a crowd is quite different from dancing before one, Adele. This is my debut on the lecture circuit."

Adele calmly fixed a stray lock of frosted hair that bobbed over her forehead. "Doesn't the Learning Center offer any courses on public speaking?" She rested her hands in her lap and smiled. "With a business community like we have on Long Island, that was the first course I listed in my syllabus."

Larkin took a deep breath. "I guess my business acumen isn't quite as well developed as yours." She called up the friendliest smile she could manage. "Perhaps I should have signed up for a course or two at your school."

George, the continuing-education director at Hofstra University, threw his head back and laughed. "Touché, Adele! Looks like the new kid on the block is catching on."

Adele immediately redirected her bad mood toward him.

This was not the time or place to get into a verbal sparring match with a heavyweight champion like Adele Masters. Larkin's nerves were too badly frayed for her to stand a chance. She slipped out into the hallway and tried to calm herself down by pacing the narrow corridor.

Larkin was a participant in an all-day seminar called "Single in America: View for the Eighties," which was being held at the Sheraton Smithtown on Long Island. When her assistant, Patti Franklin, had presented the idea to Larkin, it had sounded like a fantastic way to reach a larger section of the public. Now that it was almost her turn to take the stage, Larkin questioned her own wisdom. She could barely remember her own name, much less her speech.

"Never again," she said aloud. "Not unless I'm tranquilized first."

"Cold feet?" she heard Patti's familiar voice behind her.

"Cold feet, cold hands and a cold heart," Larkin said, turning to look at the flamboyant redhead in a cobalt-blue minidress.

"I don't understand you, Larkin," Patti said, shaking her tangled mass of curls. Her enormous yellow earrings looked like UFOs. "You've danced before thousands, and you can't manage a simple speech?"

Where have I heard that before? "Dancing I was sure of. Public speaking is something brand-new."

"Nothing to it. You just walk out there, tell them what you plan to say, say it, then wait for the applause." Patti snapped her fingers. "A breeze."

"Easy for you to say, hiding behind that clipboard." Larkin extended her speech notes toward the younger woman with a grin. "Why don't you stand up there and promote the Learning Center for me?"

"Why give the audience chopped liver when they're expecting caviar? They'd probably throw tomatoes at me."

Larkin swatted the woman over the head with the deck of index cards. "Why should they bother to throw tomatoes at you? You're always the first one in line to throw them at yourself. I wish to heaven you would—"

"Don't tell me; I already know it by heart. Believe in myself, stop putting myself down, lose twenty pounds . . ."

"I never said you should lose twenty pounds."

"I just thought I'd slip that in. Tim said—"

"I don't care what Tim said. If only you'd stop going out with these rejects from the Disco Hall of Fame, you might have a higher opinion of yourself."

"I know, I know." Patti flipped through the notes on her clipboard. "If only I took Course 307, 'How to Love yourself When You're Afraid Nobody Else Will,' my life would be a bed of roses."

"At least it might eliminate a few of the weeds." Larkin draped an arm around the younger woman and squeezed her shoulder. "Think of it this way: If you don't meet any interesting men in class, at least you'll learn something while you're there." She laughed at the look on Patti's face. "I bet you can't say that about the Swizzle Stick or The Lion's Lair."

"You'd be surprised what I've learned at the Swizzle Stick. Did you know that—"

Patti was just about to launch into one of her more hair-raising stories about the Long Island bar scene when the sound of polite applause from the audience out front stopped her.

"Oh, my God. Do you think I'm next?"

"No. I checked the program. You're on just before lunch."

"Wonderful," Larkin said ruefully. "Everyone's stomach will be rumbling, and they'll be so cranky I'll probably be booed off the stage in favor of tuna surprise."

"Whatever happened to positive thinking?"

"I'm positive I'll forget why I'm up there; I'm positive I'll get so tongue-tied that it will take three dentists an hour to untangle my mouth."

Patti grabbed the index cards from Larkin and arranged them in the proper sequence. "You'll be a smash if you'll just relax." She put the cards into the deep pocket of her dress. "Get your mind off your speech for a little while."

Larkin resumed pacing the hallway, with Patti jogging to keep up with her. "Who's holding down the fort? We have two classes this afternoon and—"

"Vivian is at the reception desk, Sharon is doubling as registrar, and both instructors say they'll be in, despite the rain."

"Did you call the roofer about the leak in the rear classroom?" Larkin had noticed a small rupture in the ceiling during the last spell of rain and kept neglecting to have it taken care of.

A slow, pleased smile spread across Patti's round face. "Gordon heard me tell Vivian about it, and next thing I knew, he was up on the roof checking it out."

Gordon Franklin had been working for Larkin and the Learning Center for two months as a general handyman and messenger.

"You realize your brother is incredible, don't you, Patti? He seems to know what has to be done before I do."

"And you realize I'll never be able to repay you for giving him a chance, don't you? The change in him is nothing short of miraculous."

Patti's gratitude embarrassed Larkin, and she was about to change the subject when one of the seminar directors burst out of the waiting room.

"Come on, Learning Center, move it! The guy from Hofstra is in the john tossing his cookies. You're on next."

Panic whipped through Larkin.

"I can't," she said to Patti. "I have to run through the speech again. I didn't even get to—"

Patti placed the pack of index cards in Larkin's hand.

"Thirty seconds, Walker. Let's go!"

Patti propelled Larkin through the waiting room and toward the entrance to the auditorium stage.

"Pretend this is Radio City Music Hall," Patti whispered in her ear as the introduction began. "Pretend you're in your spangled leotard and it's just another performance."

"And please welcome Ms Larkin Walker."

Larkin straightened her shoulders, smoothed her hair back and searched her memory for her best theatrical smile. "Like this?"

Patti gave her the thumbs-up sign. "Perfect," she said. "Now, go break a leg!"

ALEX JAKOBS, Ph.D., slid his long body lower in the chair and let his eyes droop shut.

"Sit up, Jakobs," the gruff voice next to him muttered. "You're giving the press a bad name."

"Quiet, Harry," he said to the older man. "I'm not the press. Besides, this is the first good sleep I've had in a week. This seminar is better than Valium."

Alex had just suffered through six workshops filled with the strangest conglomeration of material he'd ever seen presented in one place: advice from jaded divorcées on the realities of romance; talks from bartenders on "you are what you drink"; and a panel presentation on the single consumer and his or her fiscal power. All of that, and it wasn't even lunchtime yet.

Alex glanced to his right at the crowd of single men and women, all of whom had paid seventy-five dollars a head to sit there and listen to what they already knew all too well: loneliness was big business. All the talk of a sexual revolution, the joys of freedom, the fun of an unfettered relationship fell apart before the anxiety visible on every face in the room.

And how well Alex understood it all. It was hard to settle for just sex when you've known what it was like to make love.

Harry, the photographer, next to him, muffled a yawn with the back of his hand, and Alex's serious face ignited with a grin.

"You dozing off on me, Harry? You know Mathison is expecting a full photo spread to go with my feature."

"If you get a feature out of this malarkey, you deserve a Pulitzer along with your Ph.D., Jakobs." He uttered a mild oath that made Alex laugh out loud. "This is how I get paid for twenty-five years of loving devotion to *Metro Monthly*?"

Alex pulled off his suit jacket and draped it over the back of the empty seat in front of him. "No," he answered as he loosened his burgundy-colored knit tie. "This is how I get paid for agreeing to do Mathison a favor. I'd rather be flying." Normally Alex spent his Thursday mornings flying his Cessna and thinking about his cable-TV show that aired every Thursday night.

Mathison, the editor of *Metro Monthly*, a New York metropolitan-area magazine, had thought Alex Jakobs, noted therapist and old friend, would be the perfect writer to handle the singles' seminar.

"You're the only single guy I know who can string two words together," he'd explained, trying to convince Alex that he could have more fun at the Sheraton than behind the controls of his plane. "Besides, what the hell do us old married guys know from singles' bars?"

They envied him; that was the saddest part of all. They envied him the freedom that Alex would have traded in a split second for one more chance to tell Rikki how much he loved her.

As his textbooks said it would, the pain did grow less with each year, the reminders less frequent. However, now and again he'd see a woman with eyes the color of sherry or hear the sweet sound of a song from their youth, and the enormity of his loss would tear at his heart, reminding him of the true meaning of the word *forever*.

Life, unfortunately, rarely grants a man the chance to say the things he's left unsaid and, for Alex, that truth had been the sharpest grief of all.

He was glad for the interruption when Harry let loose with a slow whistle and began looking for his camera on the floor between their chairs.

"Things are definitely looking up," Harry said. He moved into the side aisle to get a shot.

A tall, slender woman of about thirty glided toward the podium. A chorus of whistles and good-naturedly ribald remarks accompanied her approach, but she managed to remain unruffled by them. A small, amused smile twitched at the corners of her mouth. Alex sat up straighter and began scribbling notes in his own peculiar form of shorthand.

"Knit T-shirt dress, color of a ripe tomato...wide leather belt...high heels...great legs."

It wasn't much of a dress, really. It seemed to have no structure at all, simply flowing over her curves in a very intriguing fashion. It was the kind of dress that depended upon the woman who wore it to bring it to life. This woman managed to make it sparkle with unmistakable flair and sophistication.

She was fine-boned and fair-skinned, and her Renaissance face was wreathed by a cloud of sandy-blond waves that tumbled almost to her waist. He didn't know if it was the lighting or a gift from a generous god, but her hair seemed shot through with golden lights that shimmered beneath the fluorescent fixture overhead.

He glanced at the other people sitting up there on the stage. No, it was a gift from the gods, all right. Fluorescent lights made everyone else look green.

He glanced again at the agenda. She had to be the woman from the Olympia Health Spa. No one could have a body as gently yet strongly curved as hers unless she gave it the attention due a full-time job. Yes, he thought as he watched her arrange her notes in a neat pile at the stand and let her enormous eyes scan the room slowly while she collected her thoughts, he could easily imagine her in a tight-fitting leotard.

"You're right, Harry," he murmured. "Things are definitely looking up."

LARKIN'S SMILE masked her nervous tension. *I should have worn the spangled leotard,* she thought.

The walk across the stage to the podium was the longest one of her life. Quickly she gauged the distance between herself and the fire exits. If things got tough, it was nice to know that she was only eighty feet from freedom.

"Have you ever imagined sailing over the countryside in a hot-air balloon or drifting over the estates on the North

Shore in a free-flying glider? Do you have a yen to learn French or take up ballet? If you've dreamed of any of these things, but are convinced you're too busy or too tired or too old to try them, I'm here to tell you that at the Learning Center anything is possible."

Nothing. Not a smile, not a nod, no reaction at all. Something was definitely wrong.

"Learning isn't confined within the walls of a university or..."

Larkin searched the audience for the slightest sign of encouragement. An overweight red-haired man snoozed in an aisle seat, his lower jaw sagging open. A young blond woman in the first row was hanging on to her purse as if it were the lifeline on the *Titanic*.

Her speech was turning out to be a bigger bomb than the MX missile.

In the wings Patti coughed, and Larkin glanced over in time to see her do a wonderful imitation of the sleeping man.

That does it, Franklin. Next time you will *make the speech.*

She droned on, "Two hours a week can change your life." She'd sell her soul for one friendly face, one person who seemed to understand what she was trying to say.

Then, suddenly, Larkin saw him. The fifth row, center. About thirty-five, dark brown hair graying slightly at the temples, neatly trimmed beard and mustache. He was the picture of the powerful businessman in his expensive silk shirt, the kind of man who should be up there on the podium instead of Larkin. He was watching her intently, leaning forward in his seat as if to catch every word.

"The boundaries you set during your nine-to-five life needn't restrict you after you..."

Larkin couldn't resist meeting the dark-haired man's eyes again. He smiled, and she saw the flash of white teeth, felt the quick jolt of energy that radiated from him. He was listening, really listening, to what she had to say.

This brief flash of one-to-one communication reminded her of her days in the corps de ballet, when she was one of a group of nameless, faceless dancers whose main job was to preserve their anonymity as a backdrop to the prima ballerina. Sometimes, though, she would catch the eye of one person in the audience, one wonderful person who somehow acknowledged Larkin's own uniqueness. Someone who made it worthwhile.

Like this man in the fifth row, center.

She took a deep breath and let the remaining index cards fall to the floor at her feet.

Patti's backstage groan could be heard all the way to the rafters.

"How many of you came here to meet somebody?" Silence. "Come on," she said, walking along the lip of the stage, "I know you've all come to this singles' seminar for a reason, and I'll bet it's not to learn how to conjugate Latin verbs." More laughter, but this time it was easier and louder.

"Can we talk?" she asked, à la Joan Rivers. "Be honest. How many came here today hoping it was an all-day happy hour?"

A woman in a green feathered hat raised her hand; a man on the aisle raised his—in moments, the auditorium was a sea of hands.

"That's what I was afraid of," she said. "Well, if all you want out of life is a body next to yours each night, then maybe this is your chance to go outside for a cup of coffee, because that's not what I want to talk to you about."

Larkin headed back to the lectern, took a sip of water and looked out at the audience. No one had left. In fact, it seemed that no one had so much as blinked.

Well, I'll be damned, she thought. *So this is what public speaking is all about.*

"Loneliness is big business," she said, choosing her words carefully. "Most of us on the program today make a living off loneliness with promises of matches made in heaven and nights of ecstasy, if you only take this cruise or join that health spa." She paused for effect. "I can't promise you anything."

She let her gaze slowly travel the room, and once again, she was drawn to the darkly handsome man with the silky beard who had been giving her his undivided attention. His gaze was level and direct, with none of the preening, obvious looks of a man on the make. It was a serious face as well as a handsome one, and she had the impression of a dynamic brain at work behind those intense eyes. She didn't know if it was her romantic nature or not, but there seemed to be a slightly haunted look to him, a vague shadow of something that made her yearn to hold him in her arms.

This was not the time, though, for romantic fantasies, no matter how pleasant.

"I can't promise you'll meet the man of your dreams taking French at the Learning Center, or that Linda Evans's twin sister will be sitting next to you at one of our 'Great Books' discussions. The only thing I can promise you is that if you give us some of your spare time, we'll send you home each night with much more than the memory of five vodka martinis and four hours of half-witted, half-heard conversation—we'll send you home with ideas. We'll send you home with dreams."

The audience burst into spontaneous applause, and Larkin sought out the eyes of the man in the fifth row.

He was still watching her, his handsome face serious and intense. Then, suddenly he broke into a smile so dazzling that her stomach took the express elevator to her feet.

You did it, his look said. *You won them over. Congratulations.*

She smiled back at him, acknowledging her triumph, then settled down to make the speech of her life.

SHE WAS INCREDIBLE. Absolutely incredible.

But, of course, Alex had known that the second she glided across the stage with a kind of magical star quality that defied even his most logical mind. There was no getting away from the fact that she was sexy as hell—half the men in the audience would have hocked their Rolexes to spend an hour with her—but it went beyond the obvious for Alex, even though the obvious was quite appealing.

He found himself as fascinated by what Larkin Walker had to say as he was fascinated by the terrific way she looked when she said it.

"Get a load of those legs," Harry, beside him, mumbled as Larkin strode the length of the stage, pulling the audience into her speech by the sheer force of her personality. "I wonder how they'd—"

"Shut up," Alex snapped.

Harry turned to him, a look of surprise and amusement on his weathered face.

"Sorry." Alex had surprised himself with the suddenness and force of his remark. "I want to hear what she's saying."

Harry's bushy eyebrows arched over the tops of his glasses but he said nothing, which made Alex even more uncomfortable. His reputation for being cool, logical Dr. Jakobs was being shot to hell, but at the moment he didn't care. All his concentration was zeroed in on the woman with the cloud of angel's hair who was wrapping the audience—and a very surprised Alex—around her little finger.

IT WAS GOING BETTER than Larkin's wildest dreams.

From the second she tossed aside her index cards and began to speak from the heart, they had been ripe for the plucking. The shield of boredom that had separated the audience from her had lifted, and she felt as if her words were really meeting their mark.

And even though she tried hard not to be obvious, she was again and again drawn to the enigmatic man in the fifth row whose intense eyes had been riveted to her from the moment she came out onstage.

She paused, her gaze scanning the crowd, then once again focusing in on him. He was leaning forward in his seat, as if he wanted to bridge the distance between them.

She stepped away from the lectern and walked over to the edge of the stage. "Follow your own dreams; expand your world by learning new skills or seeking out new experiences." She took a deep breath. "You only live once, and if you do it right, that can be enough. I promise you the Learning Center can help you do it right. Thank you."

Now where on earth was the applause?

Her stomach lurched sideways, and a pulse in her throat hammered so hard that she prayed someone in the audience knew CPR. She glanced offstage, expecting at least to see Patti applauding her, but apparently even her devoted assistant had abandoned the sinking ship.

She straightened her shoulders and was about to leave with whatever shreds of dignity she could muster, when the audience exploded into a thousand questions, and it seemed as if they were all directed right at her.

Mac Mulrooney, the emcee, was still onstage, and he beamed at her as if he'd just discovered uranium in his driveway.

"Go for it," he whispered. "You got 'em right where you want 'em."

Larkin pointed to a man in the second row who wore enough gold around his neck to balance the deficit.

"What's your phone number?"

"The Learning Center's phone number is in the brochure you got at registration. Call me anytime you need class information."

The woman in the green hat with the blue feather raised her hand. "Do you teach belly dancing?"

"Only tap dancing, right now, but I'll note your request."

She caught some movement in the fifth row and looked toward the bearded man. He was saying something to the man next to him. His serious face was lit up by a smile and she wondered why he didn't smile more often.

"Over there, Larkin."

She heard Mac Mulrooney's stage-whispered prompting, and she directed her attention to a young woman who wanted to know if the Center taught ikebana, Japanese flower arranging. Everyone wanted to know something, wanted to learn something. Everyone, that is, except the man in the fifth row.

She looked over at him, made eye contact and smiled invitingly. "I have a few more seconds before Mac drags me off the stage. Any more questions?" *Please ask me something—my phone number, anything. I want to know what makes you look the way you do.*

Larkin held her breath while he flipped through a few pages of his spiral-bound notebook, glanced at something, then seemed about to speak up when Mulrooney, with the most damnable timing imaginable, appeared next to her.

"Okay, everybody, that's it for this session. Larkin will be available during the cocktail party this afternoon for more questions."

"Mac, I'm sure I could—"

He began hustling her off the stage. "Oh, no, you can't, Larkin. They want you in the next room pronto for a radio interview."

She looked out into the audience. The bearded man met her eyes, smiled ruefully, then shrugged his broad shoulders. Her spirits fell. Who knew if he'd even stay for the cocktail party?

"You're a cruel taskmaster, Mac," she said as she followed him off the stage. "I think you've just ruined my life."

"Ruined it? Honey, with the publicity you're about to get, the sky's the limit. Now, let's move it. You're on in three minutes."

Damn it, she thought as she stole one more look at the man in the fifth row, center. *If you'd asked just one question, I would have stayed here all afternoon.*

Chapter Two

A heavy rain lashed against the windows of the enclosed garden-style restaurant, casting a silvery-gray light on everything and everybody, Alex included.

"Is there something wrong with the spinach pie, sir?"

Alex looked up into the worried face of a waiter barely out of his teens, and shook his head. "It's fine," he said distractedly, aware of Harry's curious gaze. "Everything's just fine."

Harry waited until the young waiter was just out of earshot. "There must be something wrong somewhere, because you sure aren't touching your lunch."

"Why the interest in my dietary habits, Harry? Are you a silent partner in this place?"

"I couldn't be a silent partner in anything," Harry said with a chuckle. "You've just been real quiet since we left the Sheraton. I'm just wondering, Doc."

"I'm fine." Alex made a show of devouring a healthy forkful of spinach pie. "Just preoccupied, that's all."

"A patient?"

Alex nodded his head. One of the few advantages to his profession was this ability to sidestep discussions of his own behavior with that simple, all-encompassing explanation. It wasn't that far from the truth—not this time.

From the moment Larkin Walker left the podium at the hotel, Alex had been trying to figure out a logical explanation for the decidedly illogical way he'd been feeling, and so far, all his training and experience in understanding human behavior had him coming up empty-handed.

One minute he'd been bored out of his mind, ready to tell Mathison he couldn't possibly do the article for *Metro Monthly*, and the next he'd felt as if his entire body had been hooked up to the most elemental source of power on earth.

Larkin Walker took her place behind the lectern, and his heart thudded against his rib cage, his palms broke into a sweat, his even breathing grew erratic. All the classic symptoms so popular in romantic fantasy had swooped down on him at once and turned him into a believer.

"I need a vacation," he mumbled.

"What was that, Doc?"

"Just talking to myself, Harry."

Harry grinned. "I don't blame you. She was a knock-out."

"The woman from the Learning Center?" Harry nodded. "Fascinating speaker."

"Now, I may be an old married man, Doc, but I'm not so old or so married that I don't recognize fireworks when I see 'em," Harry said. "She couldn't take her eyes off you."

Alex did his damnedest to ignore the ridiculous pleasure Harry's words gave him.

"I don't know how you missed it, Doc," Harry continued. "Right there at the end, she practically begged you to ask a question. I may wear glasses but I'm not blind."

"Take it slow with the beer, Harry. It's doing funny things to your brain."

"The hell it is. I'm telling you, she couldn't take her eyes off you. A woman like that gives him the eye all morning, and the only thing he can think about is his spinach pie. Maybe you should have gone flying today, after all, Doc."

Alex thought of the way his spirits had soared skyward when Larkin Walker first stepped onto that stage. He'd been flying all right. If Harry only knew.

He glanced at his watch. "Let's go, Harry. I don't want to miss the two o'clock workshop on flirtation for fun and profit. That should be good for at least two paragraphs."

Harry quaffed the rest of his beer and pushed his chair away from the table. "I hear the speaker used to run a—you should excuse the expression—cathouse in Nevada before she hit the seminar trail. Some of the guys said..." Harry was off and running on another one of his stories about the adventures of his photographer friends.

Alex didn't care if they missed the madam's speech or the belly dancer's demonstration or the panel discussion on weight control and romance. All he wanted was a chance to talk to Larkin Walker.

All he wanted was the chance to feel alive again.

FROM A STEREO somewhere in the enormous ballroom, the Pointer Sisters were singing "I'm So Excited," and Larkin found their recorded exuberance a strange counterpoint to the malaise that dominated the room. She'd kept an eye out for the bearded man who had captured her attention during her morning speech, but apparently he had found more interesting things to do.

She could hardly blame him. This was the fourth interview she'd done since the radio broadcast, where she had been trapped between an aging disco king and a moderator with more on her mind than reaching the public, and Larkin was getting tired of hearing herself talk.

"I'm almost thirty-one," she said to the WPIX-TV reporter who had posed the question. "And, yes, I did dance with the Empire Ballet Company and the Rockettes."

Boring, boring, boring. That everyone was so fascinated with her dancing background, now that she was no longer dancing, infuriated her. Where were they when she was struggling along in the corps de ballet or dancing sixth-from-the-center in the chorus line at Radio City?

She sipped her glass of club soda and listened to Adele from the School for Advancement outline her years on the society circuit in Manhattan and her desire to "do something for people without her advantages."

The reporter's attention swiveled back to Larkin. "The corps de ballet and the Rockettes? Isn't that a strange combination?"

Larkin tried to ignore the murderous look in Adele's eyes. "Not that strange for the daughter of a Rockette. I could tap-dance before I could walk."

"Upholding a family tradition?"

Larkin smiled as a photographer shot another picture. "You could say that. It was nice to be reminded that dancing didn't have to be so deadly serious all the time."

"Where does the ballet come in?" he continued.

"The ballet was my dream since childhood," she said, wincing as a flashbulb popped. "Unfortunately, I was never more than mediocre. One day I woke up, finally realized it and decided it was time to hang up my toe shoes."

"Quite a story, my dear," Adele said, smiling sweetly up at Larkin for the photographer's benefit. "And where did you meet Vladimir Karpov?"

Larkin's smile faltered. "Certainly not at a tap dance festival." She turned to the reporter. "By the way, the Learning Center has a wonderful six-week course on tap. Time steps, a speciality."

Adele was not to be sidetracked so easily. "You must tell me, Larkin, dear, is Vladimir quite as—shall I say—virile as his public image?"

George from Hofstra stepped into the fray. "I hate to interrupt this segment of *Entertainment Tonight*, Adele, but I thought we were here to talk about our schools." Adele glared at him. "I may not have been a Rockette, but Hofstra has a pretty good story to tell."

God bless you, George-from-Hofstra. Larkin took another sip of her club soda and listened politely as George
outlined the success of the university's Sunday Workshop
series. Her relationship with Vladimir Karpov, Bolshoi ballet star whose defection to the U.S. had been front-page
news, seemed as if it had happened a hundred years ago. She
found it hard to remember her own naïveté, her own un-
abashed delight at being singled out by him. She had grown
so much since that time, both as a woman and as a
businessperson, that it always surprised her when someone
like Adele managed to turn Larkin's one love affair into the
high point of her life.

Better get used to this, Larkin thought, glancing at Adele,
who managed to look sly even in profile. If Vladimir agreed
to speak at the Learning Center during his New York run in
November—well, she could just imagine the field day people like Adele would have.

A camera crew joined the reporter. The female member
angled the lights toward Larkin, and a second later a knot
of people quickly surrounded Larkin, George and Adele.
Larkin spotted two especially healthy male specimens from
Jack La Lanne Health Spa as they flexed their muscles near
the cameras, obviously hoping for some publicity of their
own.

Laughter from the other side of the room drew her attention, but the bright TV lights made it impossible for her to
see anything at all. *Give up. He's probably at home with his
wife and children, a hell of a lot happier than you are this
minute.*

"It has been my experience that adult courses attract a
large number of upwardly mobile singles," George was
saying over the din of music and conversation.

"Of course they do, George." Adele heaved an exagger-
ated sigh. "That's what it's all about. Continuing-education
courses are the singles' bars of the eighties."

"I hope we're providing more of a service than that," Larkin said. "We'd like to provide food for thought as well as food for the ego."

"Certainly you're not an idealist, my dear." Adele's laugh was brittle as dry ice. "This seminar is about the care and feeding of the unmarried, isn't it?"

"Claws in, Adele. Just because your weekend seminars haven't earned back the cost of your brochures is no reason to lash out at Ms Walker, here." George raised his empty wineglass at Larkin in salute. "Success brings its own hardships," he said. "Adele happens to be one of them."

Larkin, who heartily disliked being in the middle of someone else's war, put her arm around Adele in a companionable gesture. "Do you hear that man?" she asked. "Anything to keep Hofstra's competition at bay."

"Hofstra has no competition." George rose to the bait. "We have the oldest continuing-education program on the Island."

"I beg your pardon, George!" Adele's pique with Larkin was forgotten. "It just so happens that —"

Under cover of George and Adele's spirited disagreement, Larkin turned and slipped away from the crowd. However, she had gotten no more than fifteen feet away when a deep male voice behind her said, "Bravo, Ms Walker. I admire a woman who knows when to retreat."

She spun around and looked up into the beautiful gray eyes of Mr. Fifth-Row-Center. "Well, well," she said, not even bothering to pretend she didn't recognize him. "I thought you'd given up on this singles' seminar."

"You're a very popular woman, Ms Walker. I had one hell of a time finding you in the crowd you attracted."

He had seemed good-looking from a distance, but up close, this man was dazzling. His hair was a rich chestnut color, slightly silver at the temples. The top, though, was liberally sun-streaked, as if he'd just returned from the Bahamas—a devastating combination.

He extended his hand. "I'm Alex Jakobs."

She smiled and shook it. His fingers were long and aristocratic, his grip firm and assured. "Larkin Walker." He smiled back at her, but she noted that the hint of sadness she thought she'd imagined was still there in his eyes. "Are you here as a participant or attendee?"

"Neither." He pulled a slim notebook from his breast pocket. "A voyeur."

"The press?"

"*Metro Monthly.* I'm covering this as a favor to an old friend who has the annoying habit of calling in his debts."

"And what do you do when you're not repaying old debts?"

"I'm a psychologist."

"A psychologist?" It was the last thing on earth she would have imagined.

"What's the matter? Don't I look responsible enough?"

"It's not that," Larkin said. "It's just that my idea of a psychologist is not a cross between Tom Selleck and Barry Bostwick."

"And just what is your idea of a psychologist? A variation on Sigmund Freud?"

Larkin already had one foot in her mouth; she might as well try for two. "Not exactly," she said, praying that he had a sense of humor as well developed as his intellect. "Would you believe, Dr. Ruth and Dr. Joyce Brothers?"

He threw back his head and laughed, a deep, rumbling laugh that sounded a bit rusty, as if it had been a long time since he'd had occasion to let loose like that. "Dr. Ruth? Among other differences—both major and minor—I don't deal solely in matters sexual."

"Then you must be in the minority of your profession. If visibility counts for anything, two out of three psychologists are hot on the trail of the perfect orgasm."

"You have it all wrong, Larkin." His gray eyes twinkled with amusement. "They're not searching for the perfect orgasm; they're searching for the top slot on *The New York Times* best-seller list.''

"And what about you? Why aren't you pounding the word processor?''

"I've done my share, but my area of expertise doesn't lend itself well to serialization in *Cosmopolitan* or the *Star*.''

"And what is your area of expertise?''

"Adults in transition.''

"Which means what, exactly?''

"I counsel men and women whose lives have undergone major change.''

Larkin sipped her club soda. "Like separation and divorce?''

He looked away for a split second. "Both of those things,'' he said finally. "And death.''

"That must be very difficult work,'' she said, impulsively touching his hand. "I don't know how on earth people adjust to the loss of a ''

"They do.'' He cut off the rest of her words. "They go through all the stages of grief, and each stage seems to last an eternity in hell, but somehow they survive.'' He looked down to where her hand still rested on his. "And one day, they're even happy they did.''

He knows, Larkin thought. *He knows firsthand.*

She broke the awkward silence, "The vultures are about to descend.'' She pointed toward the film crew who were preparing to swoop down upon them. "I don't think I can stand talking about my days as a Rockette again.'' She also didn't want to answer any pointed questions about Vladimir and that long-ago time.

Alex put one large hand beneath her elbow. "Come with me. I know a place where we can talk.''

ALEX FOUND THEM a booth in The Tree House, a plant-filled bar—complete with oak beams and skylights—that overlooked the hotel lobby.

"That was quite a display of broken-field running, Dr. Jakobs. Do the Jets know about you?"

"Who do you think taught Freeman McNeil all he knows?"

She leaned back against the softly cushioned banquette and eased her feet out of her black high-heeled shoes. "What can I say?" She grinned sheepishly. "Dancers have the ugliest feet in the world."

"That's not what I was looking at." His attention had been caught by the hem of her dress, which had ridden up over her thigh.

She glanced down, laughed, then tugged her skirt more demurely around her knees. "I've been counting the hours until I could take my shoes off. Those heels were agony."

He met her eyes again, the memory of that long curve of leg still vivid in his mind. "How did you manage toe shoes?"

"It was torture," she said. "People only see the fantasy when they go to the ballet. If they saw the sweat-stained costumes and the shoes caked with blood, *Swan Lake* would never look the same again."

"How long were you in ballet?"

"If you start counting from my first lesson, eighteen years. Professionally, more like ten."

He tried to imagine her as a serious child with enormous green eyes and a waist-length cloud of amber hair, but the vision was effectively countered by the very adult woman who sat opposite him.

"Why did you leave the ballet? An injury?" He had noticed that she favored her right leg slightly.

She twirled her plastic straw around in the glass. "Many reasons, not the least of which is the fact that I wasn't a very good ballerina."

Her blunt statement surprised him. "Bad dancers don't work for the Empire."

"Oh, I held my own, I grant you that. I was every bit as good as any other dancer in the corps." Her smile was bittersweet and slightly self-mocking. "And that was the trouble. I was given the soul of a prima ballerina and the talent of an ensemble dancer. One of life's little ironies."

"So you quit the company, just like that?"

Larkin snapped her slender fingers. "Just like that. One day I realized I'd never be anything special. I quit that afternoon."

"Are you usually that impulsive?"

"It sounds more impulsive than it actually was. I'd always known I didn't want to be one of those pathetic old dancers of thirty-five who cling to the company because they don't know anything else. I decided to get out before that could happen to me."

"Interesting." More than interesting. He tucked the information away for future reference. "Then what did you do?"

She drained her glass. "I feel like I'm being interviewed again."

Alex withdrew his notebook and pen. "Actually, that's not a bad idea. Would you mind?"

"Yes, I would. I'm too tired to censor myself, and I'd hate to see anything untoward in print."

"As you wish." He put the notebook back in his breast pocket. "Everything's off the record."

"I'm going to hold you to that, Alex." It was the first time she'd said his name, and he liked the way it sounded. She leaned forward and rested her chin in her hands. "Old dancers find it tough to kick the habit cold turkey, so I joined the Rockettes for a while."

She told him about her mother, who had performed with the famed precision dancers at one time.

"What made you quit there?"

Silence for a long moment. "I hurt my knee," she said. "I had surgery and could have gone back, but I'd had my fill of pain and decided to hang up my tap shoes permanently.''

"Regrets?"

"Not a one." She smiled at him. "Once I decided I didn't have to live with pain, the rest came easy."

Alex looked at her sharply. Psychologists worked as much on intuition as intellect, and his intuition told him that Larkin Walker was neither as uncomplicated nor quite as happy as she had seemed at first glance.

"It takes most people years to realize they don't have to live with pain," he said, smiling back at her. "My profession is predicated on that truth."

"Most people aren't dancers." She pushed the heavy waves of amber hair from her narrow face. "We understand pain intimately." Her eyes lingered on his a bit longer than he had expected; the look in them told Alex that she recognized that he saw more than she cared to reveal.

The waiter brought Larkin a fresh glass of club soda with a twist of lime and another vodka for Alex.

"And so, Dr. Jakobs," she said, leaning back in her seat and fastening those wonderful eyes on him, "we turn the spotlight on you. It would seem you are a man of many talents: doctor, writer—" she grinned "—football player."

"Scratch the last one. At my age, players are being retired, not drafted."

Larkin narrowed her eyes as she appraised him. "You have a little silver at the temples and a few laugh lines here and there, but all in all, you don't seem in any danger of running out of steam yet." He frowned at her and she laughed. "What are you—thirty-five?"

"Thirty-six. And the least you could do is say I'm well preserved."

"You're very well preserved, Doctor. I'd like your secret."

He was about to invent a regimen of yogurt and vitamins when a small, round red-haired woman rushed up to the table. She glanced at Alex once, briefly, then turned back and appraised him in a manner that was so blatantly sexual that he had to laugh.

"This is Patti Franklin," Larkin said, with a what-can-I-do look on her face. "She's my assistant at the Learning Center. Patti, if you can quit staring, this is Dr. Alex Jakobs."

"I know you," Patti said, giving him her best smile. "You're on cable, aren't you?"

Alex shook her hand and nodded. "Guilty," he said, looking over at Larkin. "Every Thursday night."

"I never miss you," Patti continued. "I really like the segments on sexuality."

Larkin laughed into her drink, and Alex's face reddened. "What can I tell you?" He shrugged as nonchalantly as he could manage. "Sex sells, and we need the ratings."

"Should Dr. Ruth be looking over her shoulder?" Larkin asked.

"You bet she should," Patti answered. She was eyeing Alex so intently that he felt like a dancer at Chippendale's. "I've taped all of your shows. In fact, that last one on how to help a man to—"

Larkin cleared her throat. "Patti, wasn't there something you wanted to speak with me about?" Alex thanked her silently for the reprieve.

"Oh, yes, there was." Patti cast one last look at Alex. "Mac Mulrooney wants all the speakers to sit in on an impromptu panel discussion."

"Anything but that, Patti, please. I can't take another panel."

Patti's flirtatious manner fell away from her like an extra sweater. "It's great publicity. Besides, there's a rumor that someone from *Time* is covering this workshop."

"Can you promise me a cover story?" Larkin asked.

"Yes," Patti said, winking at Alex. "A cover story and a five-page spread inside."

"Ah, Patti, you're a terrible liar."

Patti leaned against the edge of the booth and plucked the lime out of Larkin's glass. Alex was beginning to see that, beneath the brashness, the young woman was businesslike and held her employer in great esteem. "Will you do it?"

Larkin looked at Alex and gave a gesture of defeat. "You win. When do they need me?"

"Five minutes ago." Now that her mission was accomplished, Patti was her outrageous self again and gave Alex a sizzling look. "I had a hell of a time tracking down you and Dr. Wonderful."

Larkin looked as though she wanted to slide right under the table, but Alex burst out laughing.

"If you ever need a job doing PR work, Patti, let me know. I could use someone like you on my side."

Patti gave him a cocky grin and sidled over to his side of the booth.

"Now, wait a minute!" Larkin's voice rippled with laughter. "Don't you go stealing my ace employee out from under me, Dr. Jakobs. That's no way to start off a friendship."

Before he could think of something suitably witty to say, Patti jumped in. "Sorry, Doctor, but I'm with Larkin for as long as she wants me." Her round face grew serious. "Do you know that when I was down and out, Larkin offered me this job and—"

"No hearts and flowers, Franklin," Larkin interrupted. "I thought we were in a rush."

"We are. It's just that both Gordon and I—"

Alex frowned. "Gordon?"

"My brother," Patti said. "Gordon's had a tough time of it, too, and Larkin gave him a job. She's the most—"

Larkin clamped her hands over her ears. "I can't take any more of this, Patti." She looked at Alex and rolled her eyes. "She makes me sound like Mother Teresa."

Alex could tell that Patti had only been warming up to her subject, but she acceded to Larkin's wishes.

She tapped her bright magenta nails on the tabletop. "They're setting up in the Suffolk Room. If you don't want one of the end seats, you should get moving."

Don't go, Alex thought. *We're only getting started.*

Larkin hesitated a moment. "You go ahead, Patti. Tell them I'll be right there."

Patti looked at Alex. A small smile tilted the corners of her mouth. "I'll tell them."

Alex wondered if he were really that transparent.

"Five minutes, Larkin." She hurried off through the bar, her hip-swinging walk attracting attention from a group of salesmen at a corner table.

"Patti takes a little getting used to," Larkin said as she gathered up her pocketbook and smoothed her hair with the back of her hand. "Believe it or not, she's the best assistant I've ever had."

"I believe it. She seems to think pretty highly of you, too."

Larkin shrugged. "A lot of that has to do with giving her brother a job. I was just glad I could help." She slid gracefully out of the booth and stood up, straightening the skirt of her red dress.

Alex threw some money down on the table. Larkin's heels made her taller than average, but even so, she came only up to his shoulder. He wondered how she would feel in his arms.

"I don't think this will take too long. We could always finish our conversation after, if you'd like."

"Name the—" His high spirits fizzled. "Damn it. It's Thursday. I have a taping tonight."

She didn't even try to hide her disappointment, and he was touched by that. Somehow she seemed to have gotten through thirty years of living without acquiring that hard shell most people used to shield their emotions.

"You could come to the studio," he said.

"The studio?"

"We could go out to dinner after the taping." *Slow down, Jakobs. You sound like you're sixteen years old.*

"I'm sorry, but I can't. I have other plans."

"I see."

"I don't think you do. My brother keeps setting up these ridiculous blind dates for me. If I could get in touch with this man, I would—"

"You don't have to explain anything to me, Larkin." Alex's voice sounded gruff even to his own ears. The softness of her touch was doing strange things to his emotions, making him feel things he'd thought himself well past. A vision of her in the arms of another man switched on inside his head, and despite his cool words, a hot coil of anger stirred inside him. "Maybe another time."

"Tomorrow?" His face must have registered his surprise, because Larkin quickly backtracked. "I'm only teasing," she said. "We could exchange phone numbers and work something out next week."

"I'm flying down to Virginia tomorrow to spend the weekend with some old friends, or that would have been terrific."

"You don't have to explain anything to me, Alex," she said, gently turning his own words back on him. "You're allowed to have other plans." Her smile, though, wasn't quite as bright as it had been before. "I'll give you my number."

He handed her his notebook and pen and she scribbled something in the upper margin of the first page.

"I have an answering machine," she said as she handed the notebook back to him. "You're not one of those fanatics who hates tape recorders, are you?"

"Don't worry," he said, pulling out one of his business cards and handing it to her, "I promise I'll leave a message."

"I'll be counting on that." Larkin kissed his cheek. The lush, female scent of Bal à Versailles called up some vividly erotic images.

Before Alex could say anything more, Larkin thanked him for the drink, then turned to leave the bar. As she walked by the salesmen at the corner table, they looked at her the way a weight watcher looks at a strawberry milk shake on a sizzling summer afternoon, and Alex's gut twisted.

Jealous, Dr. Jakobs? Jealousy was a primitive feeling shunned by sentient adults in the twentieth century. Didn't he tell his patients that?

However, at that moment Larkin stopped at the landing of the staircase. The recessed overhead lighting picked up the platinum streaks in her sandy hair, which wreathed her face in a way that made her seem almost ethereally beautiful. When she caught sight of Alex, still standing where she left him, she smiled.

Primitive feelings of possession overpowered him. He had to fight down the wild urge to sweep her into his arms right in front of everyone in the bar. But just enough of the rational, civilized Dr. Alex Jakobs remained, and he smiled back at her before she disappeared down the stairs, fully understanding that the course of his life was about to change and that there wasn't a damned thing he could do to stop it from happening.

IT WAS AFTER seven o'clock when she raced through the parking lot, head bent beneath the savage October wind.

Her long hair was tucked inside her trench coat, but silky strands still blew free, made curly by the incessant rain.

He knew the seminar ended at four and, when she didn't come out by five, he grew worried. He'd wandered nonchalantly into the hotel and caught sight of her, laughing into the face of a bearded man with eyes the color of hot steel.

Anger grew in his belly, and he had to go outside and lift his face to the cold rain in order to remind himself that the man had done nothing wrong. Looking was not a crime. He himself looked all the time, didn't he?

He heard the engine catch and saw the headlights switch on in the late-autumn darkness. He knew the way her car took the curves, knew the way she held her head at a precise angle as she drove, knew when she was listening to the car radio by the way her long, slender fingers tapped the rhythm on the steering wheel.

He knew so much.

He knew nothing at all.

The Datsun's taillights disappeared down the empty road. He waited a moment longer, then switched on his low beams and followed her home.

It was his job, after all, to keep her safe.

Chapter Three

Never again, Larkin thought as her date maneuvered his rented Cadillac into the narrow space next to Larkin's car in the driveway. No more blind dates.

"I'm sorry I wasn't better company," she said, reaching inside her pocketbook for her house keys. "It's been a long day."

"No problem." Howard gave her another one of his wide smiles that Larkin was certain he practiced in front of his bathroom mirror each morning.

Time to say good-night.

Larkin opened the passenger door, then extended her hand to Howard. "Thank you for dinner," she said, noticing the extra pressure in his grip. "I hope you have a pleasant flight to Sioux Falls tomorrow."

"You could send me home with some very pleasant memories."

She extricated herself from his grip. "Afraid not. You'll have to use your imagination."

"If you invite me in for a few drinks, I'll show you what kind of imagination I have."

Where was he getting these lines from? He should have been a speaker at the singles' seminar earlier that day.

"No drinks, Howard. I'm sorry."

"Just a quick bourbon and I'll say good-night."

Larkin moved to the edge of her seat and swung her legs out of the car. "We have strict laws on drunk driving in Suffolk County. I'm only thinking of your well-being."

"I can't convince you?"

"You can't convince me."

"Can I walk you to your door?"

"It's only thirty feet up the driveway, Howard. I can manage." She softened her words with a friendly pat on his hand. "Say hi to Billy when you see him." Her brother Billy was her favorite and the one she saw the least.

Howard drove off down her block, and she waited in the drizzle as he made his left turn. He was a nice man despite his hard-sell initial approach. On another day she might have been able to get past the pretenses earlier and enjoy his company. But this was not another day. Poor Howard had the misfortune of coming into her life the same day as Alex Jakobs. Few men could stand up to that kind of competition.

She glanced over at Roger Lacey's house. The drapes were drawn; it was impossible to tell if he was home from work yet. Roger, who played piano at a small bar on Fire Island, was the closest thing she had to a best friend; however, his irregular hours and offbeat social life made it difficult for them to get together as often as they would like.

How nice it would be to share a cup of coffee with him, to be able to spill her tangled emotions in Roger's lap the way others spilled their emotions in hers.

She hurried up the walkway and let herself into the house. Her high-heeled shoes were off before the door closed behind her. She switched on the radio in the far corner of the room and whistled twice. From one of the deep, secret places known only to arrogant house cats, Amanda, her calico, glided across the peach-colored carpet. The cat purred and wound herself around Larkin's ankles.

"You old fraud," Larkin said fondly, stroking behind Amanda's silky ears. "You're crazy about me and you know it."

Amanda meowed and led the way to the kitchen, where the goodies were stashed. Clearly Amanda's stomach ruled her heart.

Larkin was obediently following her pet when she noticed the blinking red light on her answering machine.

"Hold on a minute longer, Mandy," she said as the tape rewound. "I'll be right there."

Beep. "Hi, this is Patti. Just wanted to see if your date was as big a disaster as mine was . . . and I have no excuse— I already knew him. See you tomorrow."

Beep. No voice. Just the sound of breathing and the bleat of a horn in the distance.

She shivered. That was the third call like that this week.

Beep. "Aren't you home yet, darling? This is Roger. No one, but no one, came out in the rain tonight. I'm home alone and bored to tears. Take pity on me and invite me over for tea when you get back—and don't say it's too late. I know you won't invite him in. Ciao, darling!"

She reset the machine, trying to ignore the fact that a part of her had expected to hear Alex Jakobs's beautiful baritone fill the air.

She was too keyed up to go to sleep, too filled with some unfamiliar emotion to be alone with her thoughts. Roger, with his acerbic wit and sharp mind, would be the perfect antidote for the bittersweet mood she found herself in.

She picked up the phone.

A HALF HOUR LATER Larkin and Roger were seated opposite each other in her maple breakfast nook. He had no sooner come in the side door when Larkin told him about her successful, albeit impromptu, speech. Roger, her staunch supporter, had not been at all surprised.

Now they were arguing cheerfully about the virtues of Earl Grey versus Darjeeling tea. Amanda was curled up on the window seat sound asleep, her stomach full of Crave and English muffins. The rain had stopped, but a dense fog was rolling in from the bay. Occasionally the sound of a foghorn, mournful and muted, broke the night's stillness.

Roger lit a cigarette and looked out the kitchen window. "All we need out there is a witch on a broomstick and a jack-o'-lantern."

"Don't forget the goblins." Larkin poured more tea from the bright-red ceramic pot. "It's really starting to look like Halloween."

"Speaking of which, my annual All Hallows' Eve pagan festival is definitely on. When the powers that be conspire to make the thirty-first a Friday night, who am I to deny them a party?"

"So that's the excuse you're using this time, is it?" Roger had been known to give parties for Income Tax Day, Groundhog Day and International Pickle Week, among others, while Larkin claimed exclusive rights to Thanksgiving.

"Be serious, darling. This is your official invitation, and I refuse to take no for an answer."

"I would never say no to one of your parties, Roger. Costumes, again?"

"Naturally. But there is one caveat, darling—no more tutus."

"I'm highly offended! I have *never* worn a tutu to any of your parties, Roger."

"I beg to differ with you. What do you call that *Swan Lake* reject you pulled out of your attic last year?"

"That was my costume from *Vienna Waltzes*, I'll have you know." *Vienna Waltzes* had been the most elaborately staged of the ballets she'd danced in; the silk gown with ostrich feathers and the bejeweled wig were reminiscent of the Court of Louis XIV, not a lake filled with swans. "A tutu!

Really, Roger. Your Secaucus, New Jersey, origins are showing."

"And your Las Vegas origins aren't? Why, darling, I've seen you salivate at the sight of neon signs." Larkin had been born within view of the glittering gaudy Las Vegas Strip, and Roger never missed a chance to needle her about it.

"You should only see what I do when I hear a slot machine," she said, ruffling his short-cropped blond hair.

"Spare me the sordid details."

"It's a wicked world out there, Roger Lacey. I'd hate to offend your sensibilities."

"The only way you can offend my sensibilities is by showing up in your tutu on Halloween."

"I don't understand this hang-up you have over a few yards of pink tulle." She reached into the cupboard and pulled out a new jar of orange marmalade. "Unless, of course, you'd like to borrow it."

"You're a heartless woman. You don't deserve gifts."

She removed the English muffin from the toaster oven and slathered butter on it. "That works out just fine, doesn't it, because you certainly aren't about to give me any." She put half the muffin on Roger's plate.

"Well, someone did." Roger opened the marmalade and covered the muffin with it. "Could Howard-from-Sioux-Falls have been so inclined?"

"What are you talking about, Roger?"

He got up and went into the hall. Larkin heard him rummaging around in the pocket of his leather jacket.

Roger strolled back into the kitchen and tossed a package in her lap. "This is what I'm talking about."

Larkin stared at the silvery-blue wrapping paper and the sparkling ribbon that decorated the tiny box. "Where did this come from?"

"Federal Express," Roger said, sitting down at the table. "Around four o'clock—just before I left for the club."

"No card?"

"Not unless there's one tucked inside."

She sat there, holding the box, her mind filled with confusion.

"Well, come on, girl. Open the damned thing! I've been going crazy for eight hours now."

Obediently, Larkin slid off the ribbon, pulled off the paper and lifted the lid on the box. A tiny pair of gold ballet shoes attached to a curling gold ribbon lay nestled on a bed of cotton wadding. A fine gold chain was threaded through an opening between the shoes and the ribbon.

Roger whistled softly. "Who have you been entertaining, darling? It seems you've been keeping the juicier details to yourself."

Larkin lifted the necklace up by the chain and let it dangle. The fine gold glittered in the lamplight.

"I think I've been keeping the juicy details from myself as well." She lifted the cotton; no card was hidden underneath. "I have no idea who could possibly have sent this."

"Come, come, Larkin. No casual conquest begging to return to your arms for another night of passion?"

She gave him a look that would have stopped a wiser man. "I don't know what on earth you're reading these days, Roger, but there haven't been any casual conquests." Indeed, there had *never* been any casual conquests for Larkin—just that one ill-fated romance with Vladimir Karpov that had left her bruised and battered and slow to risk her heart again. "I'm as much in the dark about this as you are."

"I love mysteries." Roger settled back in the maple captain's chair. "Shall we make a list of suspects?"

She laughed. "We're not solving a murder. It's probably one of my brothers or Patti or—"

"Didn't you say you met someone today? A shrink?"

"I don't think the good doctor raced from the Sheraton to the jewelry store, Roger. It *was* just a professional conversation we had." There was no need for her friend to know how unprofessionally her heart had raced during it.

"Then why are you blushing, dear Larkin?"

"A physiological quirk."

"I don't believe it."

"For heaven's sake, Roger, let up. I'm as much in the dark about this gift as you are."

"You wouldn't mind, though, if the shrink sent it, would you?"

She debated the wisdom of a cool, social lie, then decided that their friendship deserved better. "No," she said softly, "I wouldn't mind at all."

"I'm glad to see Eros is finally coming back into your life. He's long overdue, darling."

"Put a leash on your imagination, Roger. I'm sure the truth isn't half as exciting. Besides, I don't think Alex is the kind of man who goes in for this sort of thing."

"This is getting interesting," Roger said. "What sort of man *is* he?"

"Intense, confident, logical—"

"You sound like you're describing Mr. Spock. I thought we were talking about a possible romance here."

"Your words, Roger, not mine. I told you before, it was a business conversation."

She remembered the way Alex had watched her during her speech—the feeling of power and energy that radiated from him had been almost palpable up on the stage. She could still see the way he leaned forward in his chair as if he could reach out and pluck her ideas out of the air. She had responded to his challenge, her mind sparking with new ideas before her lips had formed the old ones.

And when they had shared drinks in the Tree House, she had found herself mesmerized by the intensity of his gaze, by the play of light and shadow on his handsome face, and secretly pleased that he seemed to take delight in her, as well.

Not Dr. Jakobs, she thought. *When he declared himself to a woman, he wouldn't use a Federal Express messenger as his Miles Standish.*

Suddenly a wave of exhaustion, the product of a very long day, overcame her and she yawned.

"Is that your way of telling me I should go home?"

She laughed. "No. It's my polite way of asking you if you would go home. We'll save playing Sherlock Holmes for tomorrow, okay?"

Right now the only thing Larkin wanted to do was curl up by the fire in the den and ponder all the ways a man like Alex Jakobs could find to tell a woman he wanted her.

"Good show, Doc."

Alex removed his lapel mike, then smiled wearily at his stage manager.

"Thanks, Sal. For a while there I thought you and the staff were going to have to make a few of the phone calls yourselves."

During the call-in portion of the show, there had been a nerve-racking eight minutes when the phone console didn't light up once.

"It *was* hairy for a few minutes," Sal said, "but don't sweat it. Ma Bell's to blame, not your ratings."

"I got a little worried when I saw the crew splitting around the halfway mark."

"They all headed over to Larry's house for one of his all-night poker parties. Feel like coming?"

Any other night Alex would have jumped at the chance. His cool logic usually fell apart before the lure of a stack of chips and a night of draw poker. However, tonight he was preoccupied, and the thought of so much male camaraderie was daunting.

"I'm going to pass on it this time, Sal. I have an article deadline to meet."

"Larry's calling out for pastrami sandwiches. Are you sure I can't convince you?"

"Sorry. Duty calls."

Sal doused the stage lights. "We're gonna miss you, Doc."

Alex grinned. "I'm sure you will," he said dryly. "You were probably all figuring on making some money off me tonight." He got up from behind the prop desk and stretched his long arms overhead. "Count me in next time, okay?"

Sal hurried off to finish his duties so he could get to the game, and Alex headed for the office he shared with two other "stars." The building was totally quiet except for the sounds of the cleaning crew down the hall. For a second, Alex was tempted to catch up with Sal and say he'd changed his mind about the poker game—anything to avoid the sudden sweep of loneliness that bore down on him.

He wanted to believe that it was the grayness of the day that brought this melancholy mood on; who wouldn't be affected by the somber skies and windswept rains of the past few days?

"Who am I kidding?" he said out loud as he grabbed his trench coat off the hook just inside the door to his office. Larkin Walker of the Renaissance face and enormous green eyes was responsible for this mood. Any other explanation was a dodge, a flimsy excuse for the way he'd responded to her that afternoon.

He reached into the deep pocket of his coat and fished around for his car keys, then headed out to the parking lot. In the years since Rikki's death he'd been with more women than he cared to think about, trying to negate his anger and rage with mindless, meaningless sex. However, not one of those women—charming, accomplished and desirable though they might have been—had come close to reaching the part of him that Larkin Walker had so effortlessly reached today.

It had been a very long time since he felt as alive as he had that afternoon when Larkin looked into his eyes. He couldn't remember when he last felt that sweet surge of possibility flooding his senses. A secret part of his heart had stopped beating when Rikki died; today the muscles began to flex themselves again, as if daring him to accept the challenge.

And despite his years of experience delving into the secrets of the human heart, for the second time in his life, Alex Jakobs was scared.

ALEX DREAMED THAT NIGHT, his first dream in weeks.

Rikki was sitting on the edge of their bed, the pale yellow telephone dangling from her hand. He saw again the look of horror on her face, saw the image of death, sharp and clear, surround them both.

He wanted to touch her, but in his dream he couldn't move quickly enough. Those beautiful golden eyes of hers watched as he struggled. In the end, though, she was lost, as they both knew she would be.

He woke up with a start, his heart thundering in his chest like a runaway train. He touched his face and felt tears hot against his skin, and he wondered why he was crying.

He remembered no dream at all; the only thing he remembered was the feeling of impotent rage. His heart ached as if it had been torn apart by his own hands in an effort to save himself from a pain greater than he could bear.

Chapter Four

The first things Larkin did when she got to the Learning Center the next morning were to plug in the coffee maker in the reception area and kick off her wet high-heeled shoes. Patti wasn't due in until nine, and the rest of the staff would arrive at noon; she was glad to have time alone before the usual madness began.

She'd stayed awake until nearly three, sitting before her fireplace and letting her mind play with the notion of Alex Jakobs. When she finally did fall asleep, her dreams had been voluptuous—so real that her body knew the touch of Alex's hand upon it, and she awoke feeling as if she had turned a corner into a strange neighborhood.

The coffee maker began to brew, and she shrugged out of her soggy raincoat. She started down the hallway to hang the coat in the bathroom when she heard a muffled tap-tap from the classroom near the staircase.

She pushed open the swinging door.

"Gordon! I thought today was your day off." She smiled up at the young man who was perched atop a rickety wooden ladder, putting the finishing touches on some ceiling repairs. "What are you doing here?"

Carpenters' nails were clenched between his teeth, and he dropped them into the palm of his hand. "When I heard the rain start up again this morning, I figured I'd better knock off the rest of the job." He pushed a strand of black hair off his forehead with the side of his hand. "I'll be done in ten minutes." He turned back to his work as if embarrassed to have been caught in the act.

"I don't want to rush you, Gordon," Larkin said, acutely aware of the young man's discomfort. "Take all the time you need; this is certainly above and beyond the call of duty." She had fully expected to hire a professional roofer to take care of the problem. Gordon's expertise was a pleasant surprise. "Why don't you come down off your ladder and have a cup of coffee with me?" She motioned toward the window that looked out on the dreary, rain-swept parking lot. "Certainly this weather warrants a cup."

"Thanks, Ms. Walker," he said, his eyes intent upon his work, "but I think I'd better get this done before it rains any harder."

"If it rained any harder, Gordon, we'd be washed into the Atlantic Ocean."

Gordon smiled but said nothing, and Larkin stifled a sigh. He had been working for her for two months now, and if anything, his shyness had grown more pronounced.

"Well, if you change your mind, I'll be in the front office." She turned to leave and bumped into Patti, who stood in the doorway, toweling off her rain-soaked red hair. "What's the big attraction here this morning?" Larkin asked with a chuckle. "I thought I was the only one crazy enough to get here early."

"Believe me, it's not by choice." Patti waved at her brother. "We're reading auras this morning. The seer is due in at eight forty-five."

"I was just about to hang up my raincoat and have some coffee. Want to join me?" Larkin motioned toward Gordon. "I asked your brother but he turned me down."

"That's my little brother. Always a slave to duty." She slung the towel over her shoulder. "I'm the sensualist in the family."

Larkin laughed. "Believe me, I know, Patti."

"Speaking of sensuality, how did it go last night?" Patti followed Larkin across the hall to the bathroom.

"So that's why you came in early," Larkin said as she hung her raincoat over the shower rod. "You want to pump me for information."

"Listen, I nearly called you again last night," Patti said as they went back to the reception area and she poured them each a cup of coffee. "I figured if I didn't get to you early, I'd never get any of the juicy details."

"What makes you think there are any juicy details?"

"Quit being so evasive. What was he like?"

Larkin wrapped her fingers around the steaming cup. "Wonderful," she said, taking a sip. "Absolutely wonderful."

Patti's blue eyes widened. "He was? A blind date that wasn't a total disaster?" She staggered across the room and slumped against the edge of the receptionist's desk. "Call 911," she gasped. "I think I'm going into cardiac arrest!"

"You really should consider show business, Patti. You know very well I was talking about the coffee."

"You've destroyed my last vestige of hope," Patti said sadly. "I figured if anyone on earth would have a great blind date, it would be you."

"I hate to destroy your illusions," Larkin said, "but I was home by ten o'clock."

"That bad?"

"Let's just say it wasn't a five-star evening."

"How many stars was it?"

Larkin headed back toward her office, with Patti right on her heels. "I don't know why you're so nosy, Franklin," she said over her shoulder. "Your own social life could keep Masters and Johnson busy well into the next century."

Larkin pulled open the drapes in her office and looked down at the almost-flooded parking lot.

"What was his name?" Patti made herself comfortable on the leather sofa adjacent to Larkin's desk.

"Howard."

Patti made a terrible face. "Why are all blind dates named Howard? I suppose he wore bifocals and had bad breath."

Larkin settled down in her chair. Her toes sank into the thick silver carpeting. "Actually, he was quite nice-looking," she said, enjoying the look of surprise on the younger woman's face. "About six feet tall, light hair, blue eyes."

"No bifocals?"

"Twenty-twenty vision."

"Did this Howard have the IQ of a raisin?"

"Afraid not. He has a master's in business from Creighton University."

"What about his breath?"

"I didn't get close enough to find out."

"Well, unless he weighs more than Orson Welles and Dom DeLuise put together, what in hell was wrong with him? I've been engaged to worse men than that."

Larkin took a long sip of coffee while Patti fidgeted on the sofa. "I never said anything was wrong with him."

"Then why were you home by ten o'clock? Unless..." Patti's grin was wicked.

"Unless nothing. We said good-night in the driveway and I went inside alone. Get the picture?"

"No, I don't get the picture. If he wasn't stupid or ugly or psychotic, what was the problem?"

"There was no problem, Patti. We had dinner together and that's it. Sharing poached fish doesn't mean a lifetime commitment, you know."

"Neither does sharing a few hours of pleasure," Patti shot back. "I don't understand how you can—"

"And I don't understand how *you* can," she said. "Now, come on. There must be more to talk about than poor Howard Wallace. Like business, for instance?"

Larkin's gentle reproof was all that was necessary. Once again, Patti switched gears smoothly and filled Larkin in on all that had happened the day before.

Larkin listened, making careful notes on a big yellow legal pad. Patti's greatest talent lay in her ability to distill the events of a fourteen-hour workday into a five-minute briefing that the White House staff would envy.

"You won't believe this," Patti said, "but we have to separate the red auras from the blue. The seer says she can't work when the auras clash."

"I knew we never should have listened to Sharon on this. All we need is a race riot in classroom number one."

Patti laughed. "Can you imagine explaining it to the cops? 'Well, officer, the silver auras refused to sit on the same side of the room with the yellows.'"

Larkin rolled her eyes. "They'd end up arresting us, for sure!"

They quickly ran through the rest of the day's agenda. Patti stood up. "I guess that's it—" she grinned at Larkin "—unless you want to talk about Dr. Wonderful Jakobs?"

"What happened to poor Howard? I thought he was the topic for this morning."

"Just trying to see if you're paying attention."

"Out with you!" Larkin pointed toward the door. "We have a school to run."

Patti started to leave. "Hey, wait a minute!" she said, walking back toward Larkin. She bent down to examine the delicate pendant suspended around Larkin's neck. "When did you get this? It's beautiful."

Larkin touched the golden ballet slippers with one finger. "Last night."

"From Howard? I'm lucky if my blind dates don't present me with the bill for dinner, and you get one who sends 14-karat presents. I give up!"

"You're jumping to conclusions again, Patti. I don't know who sent it to me." She explained how Roger had accepted delivery on the package the previous afternoon. "For all I know, it could be a belated birthday present from one of my brothers."

They heard a knock, and Larkin looked over to see Gordon standing in the doorway to her office.

"Come on in and see what *some* brothers give as birthday presents, my dear," Patti teased as she pulled the young man into Larkin's office. "Take a look at that little trinket around Larkin's neck."

Gordon looked so uncomfortable as he glanced at the ballet-slipper charm that Larkin's heart went out to him. "Is Patti always so cruel to you?" she asked lightly, allowing the charm to drop back beneath the neckline of her dress. "I should draw up a law against older siblings."

Gordon's smile disappeared as suddenly as it had come. "You draw it up, I'll sign it." His eyes met Larkin's for an instant. "I'm almost done with the ceiling," he said, gesturing toward the rear classroom. "All I have to do is get the tiles over at the hardware store, and that's it."

Before Larkin could say a word, he disappeared.

"Why do I feel that I make him a nervous wreck? Every time I say more than two words to him, he takes off like a fugitive." She looked at Patti. "Have I done something to offend him?"

"The contrary. I think he's so dazzled by you that he can hardly think straight." Larkin made a face and Patti laughed. "Face it, Larkin, you've been cursed by the gods: Every man who meets you automatically falls at your feet."

A crystal-clear vision of Alex Jakobs, stubbornly refusing to fall at her feet, popped up and Larkin tried to ignore it. "What I've been cursed with is an assistant with a smart mouth." She glanced a. the enormous clock on the wall opposite her desk. "It's almost a quarter to nine. Unless you plan on greeting our seer with a towel wrapped around your head..."

Patti reached up and touched the soggy towel. With a groan, she hurried down the hall, and Larkin heard the bathroom door slam shut behind her.

Larkin leaned back in her chair and picked up the now-cold cup of coffee. Rain still tapped against the office windows, and she wondered if Alex had flown down to Virginia, after all. She was tempted to call information and get his home phone number, but there had been something beneath his easy smile, a sense of sadness and vulnerability, that made her hesitate and wonder if she was rushing things.

However, a man like Alex Jakobs was too special to let slip out of your life without at least making an attempt to get past his guard.

She'd give him forty-eight hours to make his first move, and then it was caution-be-damned.

"I'M TOO OLD for this." Alex collapsed into a kitchen chair and gasped for breath. "Anyone who thinks running a marathon is hard work should try playing catch with an eight-year-old." He accepted a glass of orange juice from Judy and shook his head. "How in hell do you and Phil manage?"

Judy Lincoln, a small, pretty brunette with a ready smile, bit into a still-warm blueberry muffin. "We're younger than you," she said. "It makes a big difference."

"Three months younger, doesn't count, Judy." Alex was seriously concerned by his lack of stamina. "I swear Tommy is turbo-charged. Five minutes into the game and I thought I was going to have to call time for an oxygen break." He took a long sip of orange juice. "Do you take special vitamins? A space-age diet the rest of the world hasn't caught on to yet? There must be some secret."

"It's known as parenthood. You'd be surprised how much energy you can muster when you have two juvenile demons on your hands." She leaned over to pat his hand. "You'll learn about it someday, friend."

"When I'm on Social Security, at the rate I'm going." He poured himself some coffee from the pot on the table. "Work doesn't leave me a lot of time for socializing."

"Try that excuse on someone else, Dr. Jakobs. I'm married to a psychologist, too, remember. Phil manages to find time."

"That's an old friend for you. Never let me get away with a thing, do you?" It was a hell of a lot easier to blame his aloneness on work pressures than to admit that the thought of trying again sometimes seemed the most difficult thing he would ever do.

"I don't mean to push, Alex. It's just that it's been four years. Life does go on, you know."

"I know. It took me quite a while to remember exactly why it did."

From high school through graduate school it had been Alex-and-Rikki-and-Phil-and-Judy, an eight-legged organism that suffered the pain and poverty of student life together. Both couples had married in their freshman year of college; both had visions of a wonderful life. The American Dream had seemed easily within reach: careers, a house in the suburbs, two perfect children and a new car every other year.

Phil and Judy had been lucky.

Alex and Rikki had not.

He'd worked through the anger and rage and denial, all the classic textbook stages of grief he'd studied in school and never really understood. Knowledge had done little to shield him from the sheer force of sorrow that hit him at odd moments and rendered him almost numb with a grief so intense that he wondered he didn't die of it.

He hadn't known that a man could feel such pain and still live.

But live he did. His rage burned itself out and his sharp-edged sorrow had finally dulled. He had managed to turn his life around and had become a reasonably happy—if often lonely—man.

It was only at times like this, surrounded by evidence of what could have been his if the fates had been kinder, that he found it hard to pretend he didn't still want more.

Phil Lincoln burst through the back door, streaked with axle grease, and mercifully stopped Alex's descent into melancholia.

"Look out the dining room window fast, Judy," he said, pushing his hair off his brow with the back of his arm. "Your one-and-only daughter is doing wheelies in the driveway on her new tricycle."

Judy leaped up and disappeared from the kitchen. Phil poured himself a cup of coffee and sat down in the seat Judy had vacated.

"First they want a tricycle, then a new Corvette." He shook his head ruefully. "There's no stopping progress, I tell you, Jakobs."

Alex grinned at his friend of long standing. "Cameron's only five, Phil. Aren't you rushing things a bit? She hasn't even graduated to training wheels yet."

Phil groaned and took a sip of cofffee. "Spoken like a true innocent. The distance between training wheels and training bras is shorter than you think."

Obviously, this was going to be one of those days where every other remark was destined to remind Alex of the gaping holes in his life. "You still have a while, Phil. I don't think either Cameron or Tommy is ready to leave the nest yet."

Judy came back into the kitchen mumbling something about speed limits, then put the two men to work peeling vegetables for dinner. Phil kept up a running line of banter about his work as a clinical psychologist working with depressed government officials, and Judy's asides were pungent and wickedly on-target. It was exactly the kind of afternoon of warmth and friendship that he flew down to share with them at least every six weeks.

However, today he felt slightly distanced from both Judy and Phil, acutely aware of his singularity as he sat at the familiar table scraping potatoes for the roast beef dinner. It would have been nice to have someone he could grin at when Judy was being especially witty or Phil especially long-winded.

It would have been nice if that someone were Larkin Walker.

During the entire plane ride down from Long Island to Virginia, his mind had been torn between vivid fantasies of the beautiful Ms Walker and the equally vivid reality of bad weather that demanded he give total concentration to keeping the small Cessna on course.

And now he wondered if perhaps he shouldn't have turned that plane around and headed back to Long Island and given as much thought to his future as he'd been giving to his past.

LARKIN WAS JUST ABOUT to climb into a warm bubble bath and stay there until her next birthday when the phone rang.

Amanda, her incredibly lazy cat, opened one eye and glared at Larkin in reproach.

"Don't blame me," Larkin said, scratching her behind one fluffy ear. "It might be for you."

The answering machine clicked on after the second ring, and the sounds of her own voice drifted in to the bathroom as she added some scented oils to the tub.

"Leave your name and number and a brief message, and I'll get back to you. Thanks."

Beep. "Larkin?" The voice was deep and extremely masculine. She stopped, the vial of perfume still in her hand, and listened. "I told you yesterday that I'm not averse to talking to machines. However, I'd much prefer it if you

were there." A slight hesitation. "This is Alex Jakobs.
I—"

Larkin raced into her bedroom and picked up the phone.
"Alex! I'm so glad to hear from you."

His voice was even more seductive than she'd remembered. "You sound out of breath. Did you just get in?"

It was her turn to hesitate. "Not exactly." She glanced at
her naked body in the mirror over her dresser and grinned.
Thank God picturephones had yet to be perfected. "I had
decided to let the machine answer, but when I heard your
voice, I—" *Slow down! There's such a thing as being too
honest too soon.* She'd made that mistake once before.

His laugh was low, and it curled itself up inside her ear,
warming her despite the chill in her room.

"Are you in Virginia?"

"Yes. Phil and Judy just went off to a play at the Kennedy Center, and I was left baby-sitting their two perpet-
ual-motion machines. The kids finally went to sleep, and I
poured myself a glass of Scotch and decided to call you."

She sat on the edge of her bed. "I'm glad you did." It was
hard to imagine the gorgeous Dr. Jakobs playing baby-sitter
to two little children, but the idea had its charm.

"I've been thinking about you since we said goodbye last
night, Larkin."

"Still want to interview me for *Metro Monthly*?"

"No, but I would like to take you to dinner Monday night
if you're free."

Monday nights she led the class in Beginner's Ballet.
"Monday's no good," she said, "but Tuesday is open."

Silence. Then he said, "I have group sessions at Stony
Brook on Tuesday."

On Wednesday they both had commitments.

Larkin wrapped a patchwork quilt around her shoulders
against the chilly air of the bedroom. She sighed. "This
doesn't seem to be working out. If I remember right, you do
a t ping on Thursday."

"I do," he said, "but if *I* remember right, you don't have a blind date every Thursday night. At least, I hope you don't."

Her spirits lifted again. "Beliéve me, that was my last one. The next time my brother Billy says he's found a wonderful man, I'm going to tell Billy to date him himself."

"The taping will be over around 9 o'clock. I could pick you up around nine-thirty, ten—if that's not too late."

"I've never been to the Viacom studio," Larkin said. "If you don't mind, I'd like to sit in on part of the taping. We could leave from there."

"After being in the ballet, I'd think watching a cable-TV talk show being taped would be a lesson in boredom."

"I don't think watching you work will be boring at all, Alex." *Oh, wonderful.* Next thing she knew, she'd be telling him about the erotic dream she had had about him last night. "Besides, you've only touched the fringes of boredom until you've spent five hours practicing your pliés. In some countries I believe it's considered cruel-and-inhuman punishment."

Alex started to say something; then Larkin heard the sound of a small, high-pitched voice somewhere in the room with him.

"Larkin, I'm afraid we have a minor emergency here. Cameron decided to try sticking her mother's pearl earring up her right nostril, and it seems as if it's taken up residence there. I'm going to have to see what I can do."

"I understand," she said, thinking about the odd things her nieces and nephews had attempted over the years. A pearl in the nostril seemed rather sedate. "I'll bet graduate school didn't prepare you for anything like this."

He groaned. "I don't think there is anything that can prepare you for something like this. Phil and Judy deserve Medals of Honor." She heard him cover the phone and comfort the child with words that sounded soothing and warm, even though she couldn't quite make them out. "I'm looking forward to Thursday, Larkin," he said. The sound of his voice sent a warm thrill through her body. "I want to see you again."

After she hung up the telephone, Larkin found herself unable to consider anything as passive as relaxing in a hot tub. The sound of Alex's voice had acted like a shot of adrenaline, and she slipped into jeans and a sweater, grabbed her raincoat, then headed off to South Shore Mall to find the sexiest dress imaginable for her date with Dr. Jakobs on Thursday, five days, twenty-two hours and thirty-six minutes from now.

Not that she was counting.

SO MUCH FOR ROMANCE.

Alex's dream of witty conversation rich with tension and promise had vanished along with the pearl earring in Cameron Lincoln's right nostril. Fortunately the emergency had turned out to be easily handled—even by a man with little hands-on experience in pediatric traumas. With some deft maneuvering, the pearl earring had popped right out, none the worse for wear, and he had been able to soothe Cameron's soul—and her brother's as well—with a quick trip to Baskin-Robbins.

It was going to take a bit more than chocolate-chocolate-chip to soothe Alex's soul.

He had dialed Larkin's number with more trepidation than any thirty-six-year-old Ph.D. ought to feel and had been appalled at the way his stomach knotted up when he heard her sweet, clear voice on the answering tape.

Ridiculous. Totally and absolutely ridiculous.

But there it was. At just the sound of her voice saying his name, he was flying ten feet off the ground like a lovesick teenager ruled by raging hormones. He knew all the names for such crazy feelings: infatuation, limerence and that good old standby, lust. He had spent years memorizing those handy terms in order to neatly categorize the different facets of human behavior.

What a surprise it had been to learn that not one of those damned terms came even close to encompassing the wild surge of emotion he had been feeling since Larkin first glided onto the stage at the Sheraton Smithtown less than thirty-six hours ago.

The last time he had felt like this, he had been a boy.

Well, he wasn't a boy any longer, and life had taught him not to put too much stock in the inevitability of "happily ever after." They were going to have a late dinner together Thursday night. That's all. He wasn't going to hang a lot of expectations on it, nor was he about to pretend he was dealing with anything more than two adults who were going to share a meal and some conversation.

However, right now, before Tommy decided to try out the pearl trick for himself, it would be quite nice to sit before the fire, Scotch in hand, and think about all the ways he could imagine to make Larkin Walker smile.

HIDDEN IN THE SHADOWS, he watched the familiar bedtime ritual of the woman across the street.

Her slender arm ducked under the orange kitchen curtains as she removed the plants from the windowsill, one by one. Next she closed the drapes in the living room, blotting out her soft amber hair from his sight. Each movement was as unvarying, as choreographed, as a dance.

He took a long drag of his cigarette and moved farther back into the shadows. Seconds later she stepped out the side door, looking for her long-hair cat. She leaned against the side of her red car and folded her arms across her chest, hugging herself against the cold.

He could almost imagine how it would feel to touch her, to be touched by her.

Two houses down, a neighbor pulled out of a circular driveway, and her beautiful face flashed in the glare of headlights—so brief a glimpse as to seem almost subliminal.

He watched her check the lock on the front door, the windows. The routine was so familiar to him; he even saw her perform it in his dreams.

She picked up the cat, and they both disappeared through the side door. He moved forward again and leaned against the streetlight. Five minutes later, her house went dark. For a second or two longer, he stared at the white house with the dark green shutters, then zipped up his rust-colored leather jacket, tossed his cigarette into the street and headed for his car.

One day he would be able to come out of the shadows.

It was only a matter of time.

Chapter Five

Larkin wasn't in the best of moods Thursday evening by the time she got into her car and headed to Hauppauge, where the studio was located in the center of a bleak industrial complex. Patti was in Palm Springs tracking down a speaker; Vivian was on vacation, and Sharon had called in sick. Larkin was left alone to hold down the fort, and of course everything that could go wrong, had. The day had been a disaster and the night wasn't looking much better.

She was headachy and hungry. She hadn't slept well the night before, and her green eyes were deeply shadowed; even her carefully applied makeup hadn't been able to hide the fatigue.

And, as if that weren't enough, the jade-green dress she had chosen for its body-clinging tendencies seemed today to spotlight every ounce of premenstrual puffiness. Cramps, sharp and steady, began as she got off Veterans Memorial Highway, and she wished she were heading home.

But then she thought about the silky sound of Alex's voice on the telephone, the way he had looked at her as they shared a drink in the Tree House, the touch of sadness in his eyes that drew her to him in a way she couldn't quite explain. Five minutes ago the thought of spending the evening with a heating pad and a bottle of Midol sounded more appealing than sharing lasagna and wine with Alex Jakobs.

Right now, however, now that she was moments away from seeing him again, it was no contest.

The winner was Alex Jakobs, hands down.

INSIDE THE STUDIO Alex was having difficulty keeping his mind on the matter at hand. Every time he heard the studio door creak open, his eyes automatically turned to see if Larkin had finally shown up.

They had finished taping one segment of his show and were now moving into a live segment, something they had attempted only a couple of times before. Sal, the sound man, was explaining the different signals they'd be using on the phone feed and Alex was finding it very difficult to grasp much of what the man was saying.

"And if anyone seems to be getting a little too weird, you just give me this sign and I'll hit it." Sal shrugged and looked at Alex. "Any questions?"

Yes. Where is she? Instead of speaking Alex merely shook his head. "Everything seems to be in order, Sal." He straightened his tie and smoothed the lapels on his dark suit. "By the way, how was the poker game last week?"

"Lethal," Sal said. "We murdered Larry before the sandwiches even arrived. You should've been there, Doc. It was a massacre."

"Maybe next time." Alex glanced at the clock. 7:57 P.M. Still no sign of the elusive Larkin Walker. The studio was empty except for the crew, and Alex wondered how in hell he was going to muster enthusiasm for another show—live, no less—when he felt as if he'd used up his daily quota of sound advice.

"Sixty seconds to air time... thirty seconds... ten... nine..."

Alex cleared his throat, took a deep breath, composed his thoughts. The theme song filled the studio while the opening credits rolled. The director was crouched down next to the camera, ready to give Alex his cue to open the show. Just

as Marty was about to give the sign, the door creaked open
and there stood Larkin Walker, looking lovelier than Alex
had imagined—even in his more detailed daydreams.

The pretaped announcement said, "And here is your
host, Dr. Alex Jakobs." Marty pointed at Alex to begin.

From across the studio Larkin smiled at him. He looked
into the camera and smiled back.

"Welcome to *Helpline*," he said, "I'm glad you could
join me tonight." *Very glad*.

LARKIN FELT RIDICULOUS standing there with her raincoat
slung over one arm, staring at a mass of wires and equipment scattered all over the cavernous studio and wondering
where on earth she was supposed to sit for the next hour or
so until the show was over. Finally a wizened old man she
could only assume was a stagehand took pity on her and
pointed out a straight-backed chair off in the corner.

Larkin turned her attention to Alex, who was talking with
one of the forty million Americans who had a weight problem. His advice was practical, realistic—certain to be of
some help to the caller, but the spark of electricity she had
been expecting was conspicuously absent.

So maybe fighting flab wasn't his strong suit. She waited
while he went on to the next call.

"This is Dr. Jakobs. You're on *Helpline*. What's your
problem?"

"Hi, Dr. Jakobs. This is Marie from West Islip."

"What can I do for you?"

"I lost my job three months ago and I haven't been able
to find another."

Larkin shifted in her seat and suppressed a smile. *Marie,
do I ever have a course for you!*

Alex leaned forward, his dark gray eyes focused intently
on the camera aimed at him. "Have you been looking for
work, Marie?"

"What do you mean, have I been looking?" Larkin didn't blame Marie for sounding upset. She would have hung up on him for that remark. "Why would I call you if I haven't been looking? No one wants a fifty-seven-year-old unemployed waitress, Doctor, and that's the truth."

"How did you lose your job, Marie?"

The woman launched into a story about new owners and tight money. Marie and her plight certainly had Larkin's sympathy, but she found her attention wandering.

Even her delight in unabashedly staring at Alex's handsome face while he took the call was tempered by the growing feeling that she should have stayed home with the heating pad and the Midol, after all.

She glanced at her watch and sighed. Next time she'd meet him at the restaurant.

If there *was* a next time.

IF HE DIDN'T know better, Alex would have sworn it was Friday the thirteenth. The three shows he had taped before Larkin arrived had snapped and crackled with style and substance—any one of them would have made her sit up and take notice.

Calls on everything from premature ejaculation to senility to chronic gambling had kept his adrenaline level high and his brain sharp. The shows in the can were dynamite.

Unfortunately, Larkin hadn't been there for any of it. The second she walked into the studio and took a seat near the monitor, the dynamite fizzled. It was a good thing *Helpline* was on cable TV rather than commercial, because any sponsor in his or her right mind would have pulled out after the last forty-five minutes of boredom. The fact that Larkin Walker was still in the studio was a testament to her innate class. If he weren't the host, Alex would have walked out himself.

"This is Dr. Jakobs. You're on *Helpline*. What's on your mind?"

Silence. The connection was still open; he could hear the sound of a TV in the distance. Another case of telephone stage fright.

"Turn down the volume on your TV," he said, smiling into the camera to reassure the caller. "The feedback can be very distracting." The volume was lowered. "That's better. Now, how can I help you?"

A woman's voice, soft and almost impossible to hear. "I, um, I want to—"

"I'm sorry but we're having a little trouble with the telephone lines." Alex motioned for Sal to up the volume but Sal indicated he had done as much as he could. "Could you speak a little louder, please?" A slight flicker of alarm passed through him.

The voice was more audible now, a little husky, as if she had been crying. "I took some pills."

Every nerve in Alex's body slammed into overdrive. He focused straight into the camera, summoning up his best professionally comforting look. "What kind of pills?"

"Seconal," the woman said. "I intend to kill myself."

THE STUDIO WAS OVERHEATED and stuffy, and Larkin was about to doze off despite her best intentions when the caller's words sank in.

"I intend to kill myself," the disembodied voice repeated. "I planned it all out. Every detail."

Instantly Larkin was wide-awake. Stagehands who had been playing poker or reading the *Daily News* suddenly sprang to life. Larkin stood up. Her pocketbook clattered to the studio floor, unnoticed.

Alex still looked calm and in control. His sense of authority was almost palpable.

"Have you already taken the pills?" he asked, looking straight into the camera.

"Oh, yes." The woman's words were slurred, the *s* sound long and drawn out.

"How many?" He leaned forward, as if he wanted to reach out and grab the caller before she slipped over the edge. "One...two?"

Larkin's heart was pounding so hard she could scarcely breathe.

The woman on the phone laughed again. "A bottle, dear Dr. Jakobs. I don't want to make any mistakes."

How many times during her years in the Empire Ballet Company had Larkin seen dancers, exhausted by their rigid schedule and racked by pain, gulp down a bottle of Seconal or Valium in an attempt to end their misery? It was obviously a cry for help, but for a few unlucky ones help didn't arrive in time.

A man who appeared to be either the producer or director told one of the stagehands to order a trace on the call, then pushed ahead of her to get near the cameraman.

"Five seconds," he said to Alex. "We're cutting off." The phone connection would be maintained, but the station would run a movie in place of the show.

It made sense to Larkin. The situation was too serious to risk turning it into a grandstand ploy for publicity.

So it shocked her when Alex, still on camera, said, "Keep that camera running, Marty. This is too important."

"Damned fool!" Marty motioned for the camera to keep rolling. "He's asking for nothing but trouble." He turned to look at Larkin. "Have you ever seen him do anything this stupid?"

"I haven't known him long enough to see him do anything at all," she said. "You know him better than I. Have *you* ever seen him do anything like this?"

"Hell, this is a little local show. The most urgent calls I've seen him handle are referrals to AA or a cocaine hotline. This is a hell of a lot more than we bargained on when we went live." He shook his head. "I hope he can handle it."

Despite her disappointment in Alex's choice of methods, Larkin had little doubt that he would be able to handle anything that came his way. She had only to look at the way he commanded the camera to know that Alex understood his power and how to use it.

She hadn't suspected that he was a man like Vladimir—a man who liked the spotlight and wasn't about to relinquish it without a fight.

WHEN MARTY THREATENED to turn off the cameras, Alex had nearly vaulted across the desk and put a stranglehold on his director. If she had really taken a bottle of Seconal, the woman on the other end of the telephone line was probably no more than one hour away from death, and the only thing Alex had in his favor was the fact that she was able to see him on her television, to watch the look in his eyes as he tried to pull her back from the edge.

That human contact, however distant, was his only hope to keep her awake, keep her alive long enough to find out who she was.

"Where are you calling from?"

"Now, you don't really expect me to tell you, do you, Doctor?" Her voice faded away at the end of her sentence. He could hear her take a long, shuddering breath. "I'd hate for you to try a melodramatic rescue. You'd really ruin my weekend plans."

He motioned for the camera to move in closer. "I think you want your weekend plans ruined." His gaze was steady, unyielding.

"You're nuts."

"I don't think so."

"Why would I want you to find me?"

An opening. He motioned for the camera to move in closer. "If you didn't want me to find you, you wouldn't have called *Helpline*."

"Maybe I just want to help your ratings."

Marty groaned, and Alex looked over at him. Larkin Walker stood to Marty's left, watching Alex intently. Once again, his professional responsibilities had to take precedence over his personal desires.

"If you're really concerned with boosting my ratings, why don't you give me your name so we'll know whom to thank when the Nielsens come in?"

She took longer to respond this time. Damn it! The pills were beginning to take hold. Why in hell was it taking so long to trace the call?

"You have me at a disadvantage," he continued, marveling at his understatement. "All of my callers at least give me a first name."

There was a pause. "Karen," she said finally. "Not much help is it, Doctor?"

No, he thought, glancing quickly at the studio crew, who all seemed to be staring back at him, as if waiting for instructions. *Not much help at all.*

She said something else, but her words were lost in a flurry of background noise on her end. Loud strains of opera filtered through to him.

"Do you have a radio on, Karen?"

"I don't have a radio."

"Turn down your stereo then," he said, trying to control his anxiety as she slipped further out of his reach. "We're getting some more feedback from the opera you have on."

He waited for a response. Nothing. He could feel Larkin's eyes riveted to him. Sweat began to slide down the back of his neck. "Karen! Answer me, Karen! Did you go to turn off the opera?"

"Can't," she mumbled. "It's a school downstairs."

"Downstairs where?"

"Don't know... second floor... somewhere."

He caught Marty's eye. "Does the school have a lot of students, Karen?"

"Mmm. They take the train."

"The subway?"

A chuckle. "No."

"What train, Karen? How do the students get there?" His stomach twisted into a knot of steel.

"The train."

Good God, just let him control his temper a little longer. "Which train, Karen? I love opera."

"The Long Isl—Oh, no, Doctor. No fair. . ."

What wasn't fair was the way this woman was drifting into death, and there seemed to be nothing he could do to stop her.

SHE'D BEEN WRONG, one hundred and ten percent wrong.

As Larkin watched Alex Jakobs attempt to pull Karen back toward life, she suddenly knew exactly why he had ordered the camera to keep rolling.

Alex understood more about the power of television than anyone Larkin had ever met. He was using that power to keep a woman alive. The sweat on his forehead glittered in the hot stage lights, but he seemed to notice nothing beyond the camera focused on him and the woman whose life he held in his hands. He had taken a cool medium and transformed it into something as intimate as a hand to hold when life seemed at its bleakest.

Her admiration for him skyrocketed.

However, the fact still remained that unless help could reach her in time, Karen would die.

The director raced in from the reception area. "What's going on?" he asked Larkin. "Any progress?"

"Not much," she whispered. "A first name."

Marty muttered a curse. "The phone company is getting nowhere. A storm has some of the lines down."

Alex caught Marty's eye. Marty shook his head and Larkin saw a brief flash of despair on Alex's face.

"What's all that music in the background?" Marty asked Larkin. An aria from *Carmen*, badly sung, floated from the studio's sound system. "She got a radio on?"

"No. She lives over a music studio."

"Great," Marty muttered. "There's only seven thousand music studios in our viewing area. We should be able to find her by the turn of the century."

On camera, Alex turned slightly to wipe sweat from his face. "I like the music," he said calmly. "Do they give recitals, Karen?"

No response.

"Don't give up on me now, Karen! Damn it, answer me."

Karen's voice, weak and indistinct to begin with, faded until her words were totally obliterated by the sound of a railroad train rumbling close by.

"What train is that?" Alex asked over the roar of engines. "What train would you take?"

"Tired . . . let me sleep."

Alex stood up and the camera angled upward to maintain the closeup of his face. "Sleep later. What train, Karen? How can I get to the school?"

"Will you let me sleep then?"

"Of course," he said, and Larkin knew he was lying. He wasn't a man to give up while there was still hope. His power and energy seemed to fill the studio.

"Syosset," Karen said finally.

Alex continued to speak, but Larkin was pulled back into memory. When the Learning Center was first starting up its music courses, she had personally visited every musician and coach on Long Island in an attempt to lure them into teaching a class for her. There were at least five in Syosset that she knew about. It was worth a shot.

Larkin turned and ran for the reception area and the telephone book. Alex's strong voice and Karen's steadily fading one echoed in her ears as the studio door closed behind her.

"Hang on, Karen," she whispered as she reached for the phone. "We're almost there."

THANKS TO LARKIN'S telephone call, the police were able to track down Karen O'Rourke to a small apartment next to Ogilvie's House of Music and Dance in Syosset, a stop on the Huntington line of the Long Island Rail Road. A squad car and ambulance were on their way.

For the last ten minutes the silence from Karen's end of the line was so complete that Larkin feared the worst. Alex ordered the camera to stop rolling after Karen lost consciousness, and the stage was only dimly lit. The telephone connnection seemed to be fading in and out. Each time it seemed as if they'd lose it altogether, Larkin found herself clenching her fists until her nails dug red grooves into the palms of her hands.

Alex vibrated with nervous energy, as if his state of near-constant motion could transmit itself to Karen and keep her breathing, keep her alive. He paced the perimeter of the sound stage like a captured animal seeking escape. All of his concentration was on the woman whose life he'd tried to save, and Larkin found herself yearning to comfort him but knowing she hadn't the right.

Suddenly shouts of "Police! Open up!" and the sound of splintering wood echoed from the speakers ringing the stage. Alex stopped pacing, and his eyes met Larkin's. She held her breath and waited, her heart thudding wildly.

Next to her, Marty Benino crossed himself.

"Doctor Jakobs?" A male voice came on the line. "You there?"

Alex went back to the desk where the remote hookup was. "Speaking."

"Yeah, this is Sergeant Wozniak. We found the victim."

Alex's eyes closed and Larkin saw a vein throbbing along his right temple. *Let her be alive,* she thought. *Please, God, let her be alive.*

"She's unconscious, but the EMT's are working her over right now. Her vital signs are good. We'll take her to the—"

The rest of Wozniak's words were drowned out by a cheer, loud and spontaneous, from the crowd in the studio. Marty and a few of the stagehands raced up to Alex, pumping his hand and slapping him on the back.

Larkin stood at the edge of the stage, watching. The intensity of Alex's efforts had transmitted itself to her, and her heart was filled with more emotions than she could put a name to. Dark shadows ringed his beautiful eyes, shadows that hadn't been there an hour ago. Finally he broke free and approached her.

"I think we missed our reservation at Mario's," he said when he reached her. His smile was warm but tired. "Sorry."

"Don't be." Larkin touched his forearm. "You were wonderful."

His expression was rueful. "Not that wonderful. If you hadn't gotten the ball rolling, the police would never have found her in time."

"It was that close?"

"It was that close. Thank you."

He draped his arm lightly across her shoulders and led her out of the soundstage and toward his little shared office down the hall. His action surprised her; Alex Jakobs seemed a man who gave comfort to others rather than one who sought comfort for himself.

Once in the cramped office, he grabbed a weathered trench coat from the coatrack and slid some papers into a leather briefcase that had seen better days. She liked it that he didn't feel the need to surround himself with the slick symbols of success currently popular.

"I can't promise you Mario's, but we might be able to get a table at the Red Caboose. It's not a five-star restaurant but the food's good and—"

"It's after ten. Most kitchens are closed by now."

"Damn it." He thought for a moment. "How about a diner? There's the Candlelight on Vet's Highway or the Townhouse on—"

"No," she said, pulling her car keys from the pocket of her coat and slipping her arm through Alex's as they left the building. "I know a better place."

"Will the kitchen be open?"

She grinned. "I can guarantee it."

Some of his fatigue seemed to lift and he grinned back at her. "How's the food?"

"I've never heard any complaints. All you can eat, great music, wonderful atmosphere. You can even take off your tie and put your feet up if you like."

"Sounds too good to be true. What's the catch? Do you have to hunt for your own steak or trap your own lobster?"

"The menu's limited to omelets and salad tonight, and you might have to help with the dishes."

"And the name of this perfect hideaway?"

"Larkin's," she said. "Larkin's Place."

Chapter Six

The drive to Larkin's house took fifteen minutes, and Alex found that he needed every second of that time to regain his emotional balance.

The agonizing tension he'd felt as he tried to keep Karen O'Rourke from tipping over the edge had given way to euphoria. Unfortunately, that elation was usually short-lived, and Alex knew it wouldn't be long before reality took hold once more.

However, at the moment he was pleased with himself, his profession and what was left of his evening with Larkin.

She turned off Main Street in Bayport, then headed farther south, leading him down a winding tree-lined street. She signaled, then pulled into the driveway of a two-story Cape Cod that seemed perched at the edge of Great South Bay. A light burned in the living room, and through the rain he was able to make out the shape of a piano near the enormous front window.

Not exactly the condo with community pool he'd been expecting.

Alex parked his car next to hers. Larkin was already hurrying through the rain to her front door, and by the time he ran up the flagstone walk, she had the door open and ushered him inside.

"Ah, relief!" She sighed and slipped off her high-heeled shoes the second she locked the front door behind them. "Here, give me your coat, then make yourself comfortable. I'll go hang these up."

She disappeared down the narrow hallway, and Alex stepped into the living room. Even his eye, uneducated though it was in the fine points of interior decoration, recognized the skill with which she'd blended comfort and beauty. The room glowed in soft shades of peach and cream and Wedgwood blue, and the faintest trace of her perfume seemed to surround him.

Classical music, low and intimate, suddenly floated through the room, and he noticed speakers unobtrusively placed in the walls. The baby grand piano gleamed in the lamplight, and the photographs atop it spoke of a history of family and friendship that, despite years of training in suppressing such feelings, Alex envied with all his heart. Brothers, sisters, cousins, aunts, nieces and nephews, parents and friends—the whole wonderful chain of human experience was right there in a collection of Polaroid shots and Kodak prints that, while not enough to send Scavullo running scared, were more than enough to remind Alex of all he'd missed.

"Looking for skeletons in my family tree?"

Larkin stood in the doorway, watching him. Her hair was loose around her shoulders.

She glided into the room with that ballerina walk of hers and pulled a bottle of Scotch from the bar against the long wall. "I can promise you there are no fugitives from justice mingled in with the masses."

He picked up a photo of two red-haired little girls with smiles much like Larkin's own. "Not even these two? They look like they could be a pair of hell-raisers."

She handed him a glass filled with two fingers of a very fine Scotch and poured herself a white wine. "Those are my nieces Emily and Rachel. My brother Billy never knew the meaning of hard work until they came along." Her laugh was low and womanly. "You think a pearl in the nostril was difficult? You'd be in intensive care after an evening with those two."

"I can well imagine."

She took a sip of wine, then motioned for him to follow her. "Let's see what we can do about dinner. I can't promise you gourmet fare, but I make a darned good omelet, if I do say so."

Moments later Alex found himself settled in a captain's chair at her kitchen table. He took off his jacket and tie; the Scotch Larkin gave him warmed his soul, while the sight of her in her sexy green dress did wonders at warming his body. He was just about to tell her how much he appreciated her offer of dinner when a large and arrogant calico cat sauntered in from the living room and with no preamble whatsoever leaped onto his lap.

Larkin turned from the stove where she was frying large slices of Virginia ham and groaned. "Amanda's spoiled rotten, Alex. Feel free to shoo her away."

"No need." He took a swallow of Scotch and let it blaze its way down to his belly. "I like cats."

"She sheds," Larkin warned as she took a carton of eggs from the refrigerator. "Your nice black suit will never be the same."

He scratched Amanda behind her right ear and was rewarded by a deep and luxurious purr. "Don't worry about it, Larkin. There are plenty more nice black suits where this came from." Amanda stretched and settled in for some more tactile pleasure.

"Don't say I didn't warn you."

"I was surprised to see you had a house," he remarked, scratching Amanda behind her left ear now. "I'd imagined a—"

"I know just what you imagined," Larkin interrupted with a laugh. "A condo, right?"

He grinned. "Well, the thought did cross my mind."

"Never! I come from Nevada and I need as much space as I can find. My dad owned a three-hundred-acre ranch way out beyond the Hoover Dam, where we spent our summers, and we thought we were overcrowded!"

"How big *is* your family?"

"Seven, including my parents."

Alex laughed. "That's almost forty-five acres per person. In my old neighborhood in the Bronx you could have fit two hundred families, three churches and a synagogue in that much space."

"Can you imagine my culture shock when I moved to Manhattan? The crowds on the subway were enough to send me running back home again."

The idea of having a home to run back to was alien to Alex, as alien as the idea of wide-open spaces had once been. He had spent his adolescence going from foster home to foster home, living in cramped quarters with total strangers who had no idea how to reach the introverted child he had become after his parents' death. Even the notion of family had seemed no more than a sweet children's fable before he met Rikki. It was she who had found the key to his secretive, private heart, and it was she who had opened his heart up to love.

"Alex?" Larkin had stopped what she was doing at the stove and her great green eyes seemed concerned. "Are you all right?"

"I'm fine," he said, finishing his Scotch and moving Amanda to a more comfortable position on his lap. "I was just thinking that the reason I took up flying was to get away from the crowds."

She was still watching him closely, and he could tell by the look on her face that she didn't buy his explanation—not totally. "Some people take up boating for the same reason."

He made a face. "Have you seen Long Island Sound lately? It looks like the Expressway during rush hour. Give me the open sky anytime."

Larkin looked unconvinced. "You have one of those tiny little planes I see at Republic Airport?"

He nodded. "A Cessna 207. I'd like to take you up one day."

"My brother Billy flies a Piper Cherokee. He's been trying to get me to fly with him for years, and so far I've managed to think up an excuse every time."

He leaned forward, smiling at Amanda's grumble of displeasure at being disturbed. "You don't need excuses with me, Larkin. But if you'd like to give it a try, we could fly out to the Cape one day."

She considered it for a moment, then shrugged her slim shoulders. "Oh, what the hell?" she said finally. "Maybe we'll start offering flying lessons at the Learning Center. Would you be interested in—"

"I'm not qualified to teach," he said, "but I can put you in touch with someone who is."

The water boiled for coffee and she turned back to the stove, fussing with filters and freshly ground beans. Suddenly the big country kitchen was redolent with the smells of ham and cinnamon muffins and good strong coffee. Soft music drifted in from the stereo in the living room, and he enjoyed watching the way Larkin's slender form seemed to absorb sound and turn it into motion. Amanda moved her furry face against his hand and he stroked her until the sound of her purring mingled with the other sounds in the room.

Outside, rain beat against the windows and the wind blowing off the bay beyond the backyard made the house shudder with its force. Inside, he was surrounded by intense beauty and a feeling of tenderness that had been absent from his life for a long, long time.

Alex had forgotten exactly how seductive a force domestic bliss could be. Now that he had been reminded, he wondered how he had survived without it for so long.

HER HOME FELT DIFFERENT with Alex in it. It was as simple—and as complicated—as that.

Larkin didn't know if it was her overactive romantic imagination or the fact that she had the monthly blues with a vengeance, but she was inordinately pleased to have Alex Jakobs sitting at her big maple kitchen table, with Amanda sprawled on his lap like visiting royalty.

Even when her Manhattan friends had called her crazy for giving up city life for a house in the suburbs, Larkin had known that it was the right move for her. The instability of her life with Vladimir Karpov had made her yearn for security, so she bought a house that pleased her and decorated it in a way that made her happy. She filled it with family and friends, music and good food, then wondered time and again why a small part of her heart always seemed to be searching for more.

At that moment, however, it was more than enough to be able to look across her kitchen and see the handsome and renowned Dr. Alex Jakobs up to his tailored elbows in calico-cat fur.

She was just about to dish everything up when the telephone rang. Amanda jumped from Alex's lap and disappeared from the kitchen, obviously highly affronted by the interruption.

For once Larkin thought Amanda had the right idea.

"Oh, just let it ring," Larkin said to Alex as it blared a second time. "Omelets wait for no one."

"I can take over for you, Larkin. It might be important." Doctors, evidently, never let a phone ring.

She shook her head and took two plates from the cabinet overhead. "Let the machine get it," she said, taking the cinnamon muffins from the toaster oven and putting them on a plate. "That's one of the few real blessings of the age of technology."

The machine in the living room clicked on as Larkin folded the enormous omelet onto a serving platter.

Beep. "This is Roger, darling."

Alex's left eyebrow arched in question.

"No one but no one is doing the clubs tonight. I'll be home early. You light a fire and I'll bring the wine. Ciao, darling." Beep.

So much for the age of technology.

Alex, to his everlasting credit, didn't say a word. He simply got up from his chair to help Larkin carry the food to the table.

"I should explain about Roger," she said as she sat down opposite him and began to serve up the bacon-and-cheddar omelet.

"You don't have to explain anything."

She noted the amused twinkle in his gray eyes. "Roger is my best friend, my next-door neighbor and the piano player at Rick's Place."

"Rick's Place?"

She detected a note of above-average curiosity in Alex's voice and savored it. "It's a club," she said. "The best on Fire Island."

Alex grinned. "I imagine that's why I haven't heard of it."

"We met a few years back at a fund-raiser for the arts. He's the one who told me this house was available."

"Where did you live before?"

"A terrible little sixth-floor walkup on the West Side. My apartment was next to a drummer who practiced morning, noon and night."

"How did you manage to get any sleep?"

Looking back, she found it hard to imagine. "I suppose Mr. L. worked us so hard that I could have slept in Penn Station during rush hour. We'd have classes all morning, rehearsals all afternoon, then performances each night. It didn't leave me much time to worry about ambience."

"Reminds me of grad school," Alex said. "I used to race from class to my night job and fit in homework when normal people slept. There were times when Rikki and I didn't see each other for days on end."

"Rikki?" Larkin looked up. It was the first time Alex had referred to anyone in his past, and she was instantly fascinated. "Your roommate?"

His deep gray eyes met hers. "My wife."

She felt as if the air had been knocked out of her. So he wasn't perfect, after all. "Well," she said, her voice crisp and matter-of-fact, "perhaps we should hurry this meal along so you can get home. I'd hate for her to be worried about you."

"My wife died four years ago, Larkin."

Impulsively she took his hand. "Alex, I didn't know."

He nodded. "I didn't expect you to know."

A million questions hammered at her brain. How long had they been married? What was Rikki like? Did they have children together? Had they been happy?

"Quite a conversation stopper, isn't it?" Alex's voice broke the awkward stillness in the kitchen. "There's no easy way to work that into things."

She started to remove her hand from atop his, but instead, he laced his fingers through hers. His hand felt warm and strong and very alive.

"I want to say 'I'm sorry,' but it seems so inadequate."

"You don't have to say anything." The look on Alex's face told her that he understood all she was feeling—both her discomfort and her sympathy. "I loved Rikki very much. She'll always be part of me."

His statement, simple and honest, touched her heart. When she left Vladimir, she had felt as if her world were coming to an end. Looking at Alex, hearing his words, she understood how little she really knew about love and loss.

"She must have been very special, Alex." *She was also very lucky.*

"What we had was special. I'd like to find that again someday."

"You will," she said, feeling inexplicably sad.

His hold on her hand tightened, and Larkin felt an odd sensation in the center of her chest. The kitchen was quiet except for the sounds of their breathing, the rain tapping against the bay window and the relentless ticking of the antique clock in the corner.

If Larkin didn't know better, she would think she was falling just a little bit in love.

THE DARK GRAY BUICK had been in her driveway for over an hour now.

He didn't recognize the license plate but quickly committed the number to memory. It was important that he know everything about her in order to keep her safe from harm.

The kitchen light was on, and he moved quietly along the side of the house, shielded by the evergreen bushes lining the walkway. Rain, slashing and violent, obscured his vision, but still he was able to make out her figure at the kitchen table. Her long hair shimmered in the lamplight. She was saying something to a man whose back was to the window, and he could see her hand in his, resting on the maple tabletop.

He could feel her touch. The glitter of gold around her throat mesmerized him. The remembered scent of her perfume was more real than the smell of the sea a hundred yards away. The look in her eyes as she spoke to the dark-haired man was the look he'd been dreaming about.

Soon it would be for him.

LARKIN'S AWARENESS of Alex was so acute that it bordered on painful. He was seated a few feet away from her on the big overstuffed couch in the den, and her whole body seemed to be alive with pleasurable sensations.

He'd helped her clear the table after their meal, loading the dishwasher as naturally as if he'd been helping her for years. Other men, both family and friends, had helped her before, but they had all exhibited just enough kitchen awkwardness to remind her that this was strictly a favor.

Alex, however, worked quickly and easily, and in record time they were seated together in the den. The bittersweet sounds of Smokey Robinson floated from her stereo, and the hot coffee—rich with sugar and cream—soothed her soul.

She sipped her coffee and sighed. "Do you know what's missing from this scene?"

Alex thought for a second, then motioned toward the hearth. Larkin kept it filled with plants in the summer; even though it was mid-October, she hadn't yet readied it for its real use. "A fire?"

"Besides a fire."

"A raging snowstorm outside?"

She chuckled. "That would be nice, but what I'm really thinking about are chocolate-chip cookies."

"You're joking."

"Afraid not. I think I'd almost sell Amanda for a bagful."

"Sounds serious."

"It is. I'm addicted."

He angled himself on the sofa so that he was facing her. She moved a shade closer.

"Tell me about it," he said in his best professional manner. "I'm a psychologist; maybe I can help you kick the habit."

She laughed. "That's the problem, Doctor. I don't want to kick the habit."

His beautiful gray eyes traveled the length of her body, warming every spot they touched.

"I can manage it most of the time, but once a month I find myself lurking around the candy counter, staring at chocolate almond bars."

He stroked his beard. She could almost feel it tickling her fingers. "Classic symptoms," he said.

"With all the advances made by medical science, why can't they manage to come up with an almond bar that doesn't go immediately to your hips and thighs?"

"If I had the answer to that, I'd win the Nobel Prize." He reached over and gently touched her long hair. "I saw a 7-Eleven on Main Street. Would you like me to get you a bag of chocolate-chip cookies?"

A particularly nasty gust of wind rocked the small house, rattling the windows. "It's too wicked out there tonight. Besides, I think I have brownies tucked in the back of the fridge." She stood up, smoothing the silky green dress over her hips and thighs. "I hate to indulge alone."

She started for the kitchen. Alex caught her by the right hand as she walked past him.

"Alex?"

He showed no sign of releasing her from his hold. "Don't go."

She laughed. "I'm only going into the kitchen for brownies. You can come with me."

"I have a better idea."

Before she realized what was happening, she was on Alex's lap, her long hair flowing across his chest and arms. He smelled of coffee and spice and masculine strength, and the touch of his hands on her back and hip was making her disoriented.

"You can get up if you want to, Larkin." His breath fluttered against her cheek.

She turned slightly so that she could see his face. "I don't want to."

"That's what I was hoping."

His face was so close to her, his mouth so sexy and appealing that she did the first thing that came into her mind: she leaned forward the few inches that separated them and put her lips against his.

The second her mouth met his, her whole body seemed to turn to flame. She saw the surprise on his face turn to desire—a desire so intense that she finally had to close her eyes in an attempt to keep at least a part of her heart intact.

It was Larkin's last rational decision.

ALEX WAS NOT an impulsive man. Rather, his actions were usually the end result of an orderly and logical pattern of thought; that had been true since his childhood. And although he had wanted to pull Larkin Walker into his arms from the first moment she walked onto the stage at the Sheraton, he had intended to wait for the right moment, a moment as perfect as she was.

However, when she stood up to go into the kitchen for those damned brownies and let that silky, sexy green dress slither back into place, he knew the right moment had finally arrived. For once he didn't worry about motivation or reaction. He needed to have her in his arms.

Alex would have been able to content himself with simply holding her—at least, that's what he had been trying to convince himself when she suddenly leaned forward to kiss him. At the touch of her mouth on his, his entire body came alive with desire both hot and urgent.

He had forgotten that anything as simple, and as simply given, as a kiss could be so damned erotic.

He slid his tongue along her lips and they opened to allow him entry to her mouth. She was sweeter and more yielding than he had ever imagined, yet the fierceness with which she met and matched his passion set him on fire. Her hands were playing along the muscles of his arms and chest, and he wanted to rip off his civilized suit and have her feel the heat she was generating inside him.

MADNESS.

It had to be sheer, unadulterated madness. There could be no other explanation for the way she was acting.

Never before—not even during those turbulent and exhilarating days with Vladimir, when she was still naive enough to believe things would work out between them, had Larkin experienced such a wild surge of desire.

The moment Alex pulled her down onto his lap and wrapped his strong arms around her, she knew that she wanted nothing more than to feel his mouth on hers.

And now that she had, now that his warm, sweet lips sent fire glazing down her throat, she wondered how on earth she would retain her sanity.

"It's a lost art," she murmured as she unbuttoned the top two buttons of his white oxford shirt.

He murmured, "What is?" against her heated flesh.

"Kissing. A beautiful, lost art form."

"Do you think we can save it for humankind?"

She pressed her mouth against the pulse at the base of his throat and savored the pounding beneath her lips. "We can try." She ran her tongue lightly across the pulse and he shuddered. "It might be a difficult job."

"We owe it to civilization," he said as his hands slid up her rib cage, his fingers lightly touching the sides of her breasts. "Centuries from now, people will wonder how man and woman expressed affection."

She could barely think as he slowly, deliberately, cupped her breasts in his large hands. She was pure sensation—she could think of nothing beyond the way her breasts seemed to swell at his touch, the way her entire body yearned for him. "We should practice," she said with difficulty.

"Yes," he said. "We need a lot of practice."

Her dress was soft and light, her bra filmy, and he rubbed his hands over her nipples. The pleasure she felt bordered on pain. She was curled on his lap, her legs stretched out along the couch. He was hard and she could feel him against her hip. Her imagination leaped light years beyond reality and she had to rein it in. It was too soon.

Much too soon.

He cradled her face in his hands and moved closer. His eyelashes were thick and dark, throwing shadows on his cheekbones. The pressure of his lips against hers was barely perceptible, yet the flames inside her grew higher.

With her mouth she tried to kindle in him the fires he'd kindled inside her. He groaned, and her tongue then plunged into the darkness of his mouth. Her hands quickly undid the remaining buttons on his shirt, and the sensation of his warm skin beneath her palms threatened to bring her to the edge of madness.

He reached behind her and she heard the soft hiss as the zipper on her dress was lowered. The room was chilly, and the cool air against her back made her shiver. Then his hands slid inside the open dress and unhooked her lacy bra, and she was on fire once more.

Alex broke the kiss—he seemed to be as breathless and awestruck as she was.

"This is a vastly underrated pastime," she said, cuddling closer. "It deserves further consideration."

"You talk too much," Alex said.

"I—"

If possible, this kiss was more shattering, more powerful than the ones before. Each time his fingers teased her nipples, her entire lower body exploded into spasms of pleasure-pain that drove her wild. Once the feeling was so intense, so all-encompassing that she nipped at his lower lip in response.

His hand slid down her bare midriff and began to ease its way past the narrow elastic of her lace bikini panties.

Reality was upon her in an instant.

"Alex, no!" She tried to squirm out of his reach.

"Relax," he murmured.

She shook her head. "You don't understand."

"But I do. Trust me, Larkin."

He cradled her against his chest, his left arm holding her close while his right hand splayed out over the bare flesh of her stomach that the scanty undergarment left exposed.

She didn't know what on earth to expect.

He didn't kiss her; didn't move to touch her in any way more intimate than the simple pressure of his hand, warm and strong against her belly. The wildness of her passion of a few moments ago changed. His touch still burned, but now it was a quiet fire, a subtle, all-encompassing warmth that spread from her head to her feet and left her weak with desire.

"Amazing." She leaned her head against his shoulder and gave herself up totally to the pure sensual pleasure of his embrace. "Absolutely amazing."

"Feeling better?" His manner was matter-of-fact, yet his voice was tender and it eased her embarrassment.

She looked up at him. "Do you have mystical powers, Dr. Jakobs?"

"No mystical powers." He kissed the side of her throat and she felt a tugging deep within her. "There are times when something as simple as human contact can do wonders."

While Larkin had almost been out of control with desire for him, Alex managed to keep his passion on a short leash, reining it in when it threatened to run wild. She was aware that they had moved from pure lust to something much more difficult to define. There was about him a feeling of barely contained power, of simmering sexuality, that she found highly erotic.

The feelings his touch stirred within her body and heart were as dangerous as they were exciting. Simple desire would have been easy to understand; this strange blend of tenderness and passion was not.

She knew she should move out of his embrace, put an end to this before it went any further, but she could not. His touch was too hypnotizing, too comforting, too exciting, and she was powerless to break away.

She chuckled softly at her thoughts. All she had to do was sit up and move out of Alex's embrace to break the spell she was under. She was no more powerless than he in the situation.

She was exactly where she wanted to be.

Chapter Seven

His body was fire and steel.

Everything about her—from the silky hair that flowed free over his bare chest, to the surprising fullness of her breasts, to the intoxicating scent of her perfume—seemed calculated to drive him crazy. In his mind he had stretched her long, lithe body out on the couch and plunged himself deep within her until she cried out his name. There was no part of her that he didn't explore—no part of him that he didn't offer to her.

He knew how she would melt against his hand, all honeyed sweetness and fire, knew how her legs would feel wrapped around his hips, locking him in the ultimate lover's embrace.

He couldn't begin to calculate the amount of self-control required for him to sit on the couch with her in his arms, half naked and flushed with desire, and allow himself only the touch of her skin against his hand. But he understood boundaries, and he understood the extraordinary eroticism that went hand in hand with anticipation, and he was willing to wait.

When they heard a knock at the kitchen door, he was almost relieved. He wasn't at all sure how much more anticipation he could handle.

"Oh, God." Larkin sat up and tugged at the hem of her dress. "I forgot about Roger!"

Alex zipped her up, then glanced at his watch. "It's after midnight. Does he usually—"

She laughed and stood up, running her slender fingers through her hair. "Roger runs on his own clock," she said. "This is actually rather early for him."

"Doesn't he call first?" *None of your business, Jakobs. This is her life, her friend.*

The look she gave him was amused. "He did call, Alex."

"Maybe I should be leaving."

"Please don't. I'd like you to meet Roger."

There didn't seem to be any way to avoid it.

She glided out of the den, leaving the scent of perfume in her wake. Alex stood up and buttoned his shirt, tucking the tails into his pants. He heard Larkin's voice in the kitchen and a deep chuckle that must belong to Roger.

If Roger were half as sharp as Alex suspected he was, he would know immediately what he'd interrupted. He might even decide to turn around and go home and let Larkin return to his arms.

ALEX, HOWEVER, had greatly underestimated Roger's curiosity.

"Whose gray Buick is that in the driveway?" he asked the second he stepped inside the foyer. "Did Patti get a new car? I always thought our Miss Franklin was a Corvette type myself."

Larkin motioned for him to lower his voice. "Patti's on a business trip."

Roger's dark brown eyes danced with mischief. "Has the Sioux Falls Casanova made a return engagement?" He surveyed Larkin's somewhat disheveled appearance. "There must be some reason for your dishabille, darling."

"Did anyone ever tell you you were too damn nosy, Roger?"

"All the time. It's one of my many sterling qualities." He took off his rain-soaked jacket and draped it over a kitchen chair. "Now, are you going to tell me whom you're entertaining in your boudoir or do I have to wander in and see for myself?"

"There's no one in my boudoir."

"More's the pity." He brushed rain from his close-cropped blond hair with the back of his left hand. "I didn't know plumbers worked this late."

Larkin linked her arm through Roger's and headed toward the den. "Alex Jakobs is here, Roger, and he's not a plumber. If you'd just waited two seconds, I was about to invite you in to meet him."

"Is this Jakobs responsible for the roses in your cheeks, darling?"

Damn Roger Lacey and his keen eye. "I had a few glasses of wine," she lied.

"I don't believe you."

She pinched his arm lightly. "I don't care if you believe me or not. Now, behave yourself and don't embarrass me."

They stopped a few feet before the door to the den. Roger looked down at her.

"You sound serious."

"I am."

"Is he that important to you?"

"Maybe."

"You don't sound certain."

But I am, she thought. *I am and it terrifies me.*

She led Roger into the den, despite the fact he knew her house as well as he knew his own. Alex stood near the far window, smoking a cigarette and looking out over her rain-swept backyard. Just the sight of his long, lean body was enough to send a shiver of delight through her. Amanda was shamelessly sprawled on the window seat, staring up at Alex with open adoration. Larkin suppressed a laugh. It was probably the same way she was looking at him.

"Alex?"

He turned. Roger stood up a little straighter and she pinched him again—harder this time.

"Alex, this is my friend and neighbor, Roger Lacey." She turned to Roger. "This is Dr. Alex Jakobs."

Alex quickly ground out his cigarette in an ashtray and extended his hand to Roger. "Glad to meet you, Roger."

Roger turned on his five-hundred-megawatt special smile. "Same here, Doctor. I've heard quite a bit about you."

Alex looked at Larkin with a funny half-smile, and she wanted to cram Roger into her food processor and set it on puree. If she hadn't been in stocking-feet, she would have kicked him.

Instead, she covered her mouth and yawned theatrically. "It's getting awfully late, Roger. Don't you have a few things to do at home?"

He gave her an affronted look. "You wound me, Larkin. And here I was about to compliment the good doctor on his cable-TV show."

The relief she felt was probably written on her face in bold black letters.

Roger turned to Alex. "*Helpline* is a damned good show, Dr. Jakobs. You should be proud."

Alex seemed genuinely pleased. "The name is Alex," he said, "and I appreciate your compliment. TV is a tough medium for a psychologist—we usually have no idea if our words reach anyone at all."

Larkin thought of Karen O'Rourke and all that had happened just a few hours earlier. "You reach people, Alex. Never doubt that."

The look he gave her was filled with such raw emotion that she feared she would cry.

Roger glanced from Alex to Larkin, and she could see the dawning of comprehension on his face. *Say one word, Roger Lacey, and I'll string you up by your own gold chains.*

"Believe it or not, darling," Roger said, "I did have a reason for coming over this late."

"You don't need a reason, Roger," she said, relaxing. "You're welcome any time."

Roger arched one brow. "Well, apparently some times are better than others," he drawled, eliciting a chuckle from Alex. "I wanted to remind you about the Halloween party. It's two weeks from tomorrow and I expect you to be there."

"Have I ever missed one of your bacchanals?" Roger's parties were usually high-spirited mixtures of good music, good food and the wildest blend of personalities this side of the UN.

Roger turned to Alex. She held her breath. She knew Roger was about to extend an invitation, but if he asked Alex to come as a Chippendale's dancer, she would personally oversee his funeral.

"If you're free, you're welcome to come to my annual All Hallows' Eve pagan festival, Alex."

Alex looked at Larkin as if he sensed that she was being put on a spot same as he.

"It's a costume party, Alex," she said. "I've already been told I am not allowed to come in one of my ballerina outfits."

"She's worn tutus three years in a row," Roger said, rolling his eyes. "Whatever happened to creative imagination?"

"Do you think we can come up with something exciting between the two of us?" she asked Alex.

His grin was wonderfully wicked. "We can try."

"I have a few suggestions," Roger said. His brown eyes twinkled, and it was obvious to Larkin that he was enjoying the chemistry between Alex and her. "All you need are three yards of Saran Wrap, four red bows and—"

Larkin clamped her hand over his mouth. "Say goodnight, Roger."

Roger moved out of her reach. "Not very subtle, are you, Ms Walker?"

"I've found subtlety to be highly overrated."

He looked at Alex. "I think she wants me to leave."

Alex was laughing. "It seems that way."

"I was just going to suggest that Alex wear a—"

"Roger!" Larkin put her hand at his back and began pushing him toward the door. "I don't think Alex needs any help with his costume. We'll work something out."

Roger sighed in mock exasperation. "Just don't come to my party dressed like *Swan Lake* and Sigmund Freud. I have my reputation to consider."

"I promise we won't disappoint you," Alex said, with a wink for Larkin.

Larkin began to push Roger toward the door in earnest this time. "I know you hate to rush off like this, Roger, but it's perfectly all right. We understand."

"I wouldn't mind a cup of coffee, darling. I can smell fresh coffee a mile away."

"Sorry. We drank the last cup."

They were in the hall and heading toward the kitchen. Alex remained in the den.

"I'll settle for tea." Roger was laughing as he was given a firm shove into the kitchen.

"No tea. No coffee. No more stalling." She handed him his jacket. "Go home, Roger."

He slipped into the soft leather bomber jacket and made a show of looking deep into Larkin's eyes.

"Do my eyes deceive me or do I detect the look of love?"

She opened the kitchen door. "Go home, Roger Lacey. I'm not kidding."

He smiled at her. "Neither am I, darling."

She hesitated. His words took her by surprise.

"Don't worry," he said. "Not everyone is as perceptive as I am. Besides, the good doctor is too smitten himself to see it just yet."

He gave her a quick hug, and for the hundredth time that evening she found her eyes getting misty.

"You know I'm here if you want a shoulder to lean on," Roger said.

"I know," she said, her voice soft. "You're a good friend, Roger. I appreciate it."

Once again he was his old self. "And well you should, darling," he said, pulling his collar up around his face. "I'm one in a million."

She grinned. "I'll remember that."

He turned and disappeared down the back steps.

When she returned to the living room, Alex had draped his tie around his neck and was slipping into his suit jacket.

"You're not going already, are you?" She couldn't hide her disappointment. "I was about to offer you some more coffee and those brownies we never got around to."

"I thought you were out of coffee."

She walked up to where he stood near the fireplace and leveled the ends of his sober striped tie. "I lied."

"Now why would you do something like that?" His beautiful deep gray eyes sparkled with amusement.

She wrapped her arms around his neck and kissed his mouth. "Isn't it obvious, Dr. Jakobs?" She let her fingers play with his thick chestnut hair. "I would think that with your background the psychological implications would be very apparent."

"If there's one thing my training has taught me, it's never to put much stock in the obvious."

He pulled her close to him in an embrace that threatened to leave her breathless. She could feel his heart pounding beneath the civilized layers of suit jacket, vest and shirt.

"Can't I convince you to stay a little longer, Alex?"

He shook his head. "I'm flying out tomorrow morning at five," he said, "and I still have a lot of paperwork to do."

Larkin felt an unexpected twinge of jealousy. "Are you going back down to Virginia again this weekend?" It was possible that the appeal of Virginia was due to more than just old friends.

"This is a business trip. I'm speaking before a group of therapists at a conference in Detroit."

They started walking toward the front door.

"Are you the guest speaker?"

"One of them."

"I'm impressed."

"You haven't heard me speak."

"I watched you work tonight, Alex. What you did was incredible."

"It's only incredible when it works, Larkin," he said as she ducked into the bathroom to retrieve his raincoat. "The rest of the time it can be pretty discouraging."

He put his coat on and she handed him his car keys from the hall table.

"Dinner on Monday?"

"I have a class."

"How about a long lunch, then? I don't think I can wait until Halloween to see you again."

They arranged a time and place, and she felt happy in a way that was unfamiliar to her. In the past, happiness with a man was built upon a foundation of insecurity that threatened to topple at the slightest change of wind.

Alex wasn't playing games. It was a type of honesty that she had no experience with; it was more the way she herself had approached relationships in the past.

A violent gust of wind shook the house. They heard the sharp crack of a splitting branch in the yard, followed by a thud as it hit the ground.

"Drive carefully," she said as he drew her into his arms for one more kiss. "It's hellish out there."

His lips found hers and the kiss they shared was sweeter than any before it.

"I'll call you tomorrow from Detroit," he said. "I want to prove flying is safe. Maybe then I can convince you to come up with me."

You could convince me to fly through a meteor shower, she thought. But no man needed to know he held so much power over a woman, so she said a simple "Maybe," instead.

He kissed her again, then started to say something but caught himself before the words had quite formed themselves on his lips.

"Sleep well," he said, then hurried down the front steps and was gone.

Larkin locked the door after him, then slowly walked back into the den, trying to keep the magic with her just a little longer. What she had felt in Alex's arms was different from anything she'd ever experienced. With Vladimir she had been grateful and eager to please, willing to do almost anything to keep him happy.

With Alex she had the strong sense that anything she gave to him would be returned to her tenfold. It still wasn't enough, however, to make her believe in happy endings.

THE DAMAGE wouldn't be noticed for a while.

Darkness and the storm had both made it easy for him to do what was necessary, and now a gash, deep and ugly, marred the sleek beauty of the car. He crouched behind two fat evergreen bushes near the side of the house and watched as the dark-bearded man raced across the driveway and got into the car.

The massive engine came instantly to life and the head-lights pierced the darkness. He leaned backward until he could smell the scent of pine surround him. The car eased down the driveway and quickly disappeared down the winding road that led to Main Street.

Tomorrow morning the bearded man would see where the car's metal skin had been torn away from the frame. He would wonder how the accident happened and would blame careless drivers or the vicious storm for the damage.

The thought wouldn't occur to him that what had happened wasn't an accident at all, that someone had meant it as a warning.

He smiled into the darkness as she began her nightly ritual.

The next time there would be no doubt at all.

IT WAS 3:00 A.M. A half hour earlier, Alex had finally given up all pretense of trying to sleep and now he lay in bed staring up at the ceiling. Each time he had dozed off, that old dream about Rikki had been waiting to pull him back into sorrow, and he had awakened with a start, feeling both guilty and relieved.

Sometimes he found it impossible to remember the way she looked. He had thought her face would burn in his memory until the day he died, and the fact that time altered his memories both angered and scared him.

Only in this recurring dream was Rikki so vivid, so real, that he could see the cluster of freckles on her left shoulder and the scar on her right knee.

He thought he had let go of her. He had honestly believed he had made his peace with her death and continued with his life. He'd spent time with many women and found pleasure with quite a few of them. Yet no one before Larkin Walker engaged his heart or touched his soul in the way Rikki once had.

His emotions were a tangle of paradoxes: guilt battled with excitement; elation tangled with sorrow. He felt that he was rushing headlong toward something he might not be able to handle, but there was no power on earth that could make him slow down.

He had a right to create a new life for himself. Rikki would have expected it of him. However, falling in love at thirty-six was a vastly different experience from falling in love as a teenager.

The teenager believes love can live forever.

The man knows nothing does—sometimes not even the woman you love.

Chapter Eight

Jayne Walker never claimed she had psychic powers, but her daughter wasn't so sure. Larkin had no idea how her mother managed it, but a long-distance phone call from Las Vegas seemed to coincide with every major emotional event in Larkin's life.

So it was no surprise at all when Sharon buzzed Larkin on the intercom the next morning and told her Jayne was on the phone.

"I wasn't going to call you until Sunday," Jayne said, her sweet voice slightly tinny through the long-distance connection, "but I had a dream about you last night and—well, how are you, honey?"

Larkin laughed. "Just fine, Mom. How are you and Daddy doing?"

Jayne told her about her father's latest land deal in the northern part of the state. "He's trying to push through all the paperwork so we can break away over the holidays."

Larkin nodded her thanks as Sharon put a steaming cup of coffee down on her desk. For once the office was quiet: Patti was still in Palm Springs, Vivian wasn't due in until noon, and Gordon had called in sick. It was a welcome change from the normal insanity.

"Are you still planning on spending Christmas with Michael in London?" she asked Jayne.

"Well, of course, it all depends on your father's schedule, but I'd love to see your brother and Naura."

Why did it always depend on his schedule? "If Daddy can't make it, why don't you go alone? There's no reason you should be deprived of the trip just because he's busy."

"Larkin, honey, you know I'd never want to leave your father during the holidays."

Larkin took a sip of coffee. "What about all the times Daddy missed the holidays because he was away on some business deal?"

"That was work, Larkin. He was never away from us if he didn't have to be."

She decided to approach it from another angle. "Don't you think Michael will be disappointed if you don't make it there for Christmas?"

Her mother sounded hurt. "I didn't call you to argue, Larkin. I simply wanted to hear your voice."

"I know that, Mom. It's just that when you start putting yourself last—well, I go crazy."

"I've noticed. You do tend to take after your father at times."

"Don't you think a trip by yourself might be fun after all these years?"

"What fun would I have?" Jayne countered. "I would spend the entire holiday season missing your father."

It was no use. Jayne Walker's primary identification was as Bill Walker's wife.

However, Larkin's experience with Vladimir Karpov and his similar capacity for taking had made her question the wisdom of her mother's way of life. Larkin had nearly vanished under Vladimir's thumb, and it sometimes seemed to her that Jayne's position in life was comparable.

They chatted for a few minutes about the business lunch Larkin had set up for that afternoon and Jayne's charity work at the pediatric unit. Larkin told her mother about

Roger's plans for his Halloween party, but she carefully avoided any mention of Alex.

"Have you asked anyone to escort you?"

Obviously Jayne's ESP was still in good working order. "Mom, Roger's house is right next door. I hardly need an escort."

"You're evading the question."

So true. "Well, I did meet someone at the seminar at the Sheraton—"

"Is he single?"

"Widowed."

There was silence for a moment; then, Jayne asked, "How long?"

"About four years."

"Did they have children?"

"Do you want his phone number, Mom? Maybe you could ask him all this personally."

"If you're thinking of becoming involved with this man, I think you should know these things."

Larkin bristled. "I promise you, if I think of becoming involved with Alex Jakobs, I'll have him fill out a questionnaire first."

Jayne, however, was undaunted. "How old is he?"

"I don't know—thirty-five, thirty-six. He's a psychologist."

"Perhaps you could invite him to Roger's party."

"Perhaps." Larkin couldn't bring herself to tell Jayne exactly how far their relationship had progressed. Jayne was intuitive enough; she didn't need further ammunition.

"It's time you started thinking about settling down, honey. When I was your age, I had five children."

"When you were my age, women had no choice."

"I don't regret any of my choices, Larkin."

Larkin sighed. "I didn't say you did, Mom. And I don't regret any of mine."

Jayne didn't mention the notable exception of Vladimir Karpov. Larkin seriously doubted if she would have been able to pass up the opportunity herself if the situation were reversed.

"Well, honey, it's time for me to start making breakfast. Jordan and Melanie and the baby are here, and you know how they love French toast and sausage."

Larkin debated the wisdom of suggesting that her brother Jordan and his wife Melanie cook their own French toast and sausage, but decided against it. Jayne's pattern of giving to those she loved was as much a part of her makeup as her fingerprints or her voice and, for once, Larkin kept her opinions to herself.

Maybe she was more her mother's daughter than she realized.

It was an interesting thought.

ALEX FINISHED HIS SPEECH before the Media Psychologists of America convention to polite applause, and he had the sudden and uncomfortable feeling that he had skated by more on charm than substance. His mind had been occupied by thoughts of Larkin Walker and how she had felt in his arms less than twelve hours ago.

"I liked those points you brought out on journalistic ethics," Pete Brennan said as they rode the elevator up to the bar, where a buffet lunch was being offered. "Do you mind if I quote you in my newsletter?"

"Be my guest," Alex said. "I don't think I covered half of what needed to be covered."

Pete gave him a funny look. "You covered twice as much as they're going to remember. Most of our fellow psychologists are here for a little R and R." Alex didn't say anything. "You know, Jakobs—recharge the batteries."

Alex knew exactly what Peter was driving at, and he chose to ignore it. He also knew that he was one of a dying breed of men for whom fidelity was an integral part of marriage.

The bar was smoky and hot and packed with psychologists trading stories with one another.

Alex ordered a Scotch on the rocks and was idly eavesdropping on Pete's conversation with a therapist from Miami when he heard a woman's voice at his side.

"You look like you could use a little cheering up."

He turned around.

She was about his age, brunette and very attractive. She held a Bloody Mary in one hand and a cigarette in the other. "'Alex C. Jakobs, Ph.D., Long Island, New York,'" she read from his name tag. "What does the *C* stand for?"

"Chamberlain," he said, taking note of the fine curve of her breasts in the clinging navy dress.

"Family name?"

He nodded. It was easier than explaining how as a young man he had felt embarrassed by his lack of family history and so had borrowed the Chamberlain from the actor who played Dr. Kildare and invented a whole genealogy to go with it.

She took a sip of her drink. "You don't talk very much, do you, Alex C. Jakobs? Aren't you even going to ask my name?"

He gestured toward the tag on the swell of her left breast. "Not necessary," he said. "You're Kathryn Anne Ryan of *Family Psychology Magazine*."

"There are no secrets in this place, are there?"

"A few," he said, "but not many."

She stepped a little closer. "Do you have a few you'd care to share with me?"

"And three million other readers? Not very likely, Ms Ryan."

"I'm not talking about professional secrets, Alex. I was hoping for revelations of a more personal nature."

He met her eyes. "I know that."

"You're an attractive man. Perhaps we could spend some time together."

"Sorry," he said. "I'm booked solid."

"Can you be tempted?"

He laughed. "I can be tempted, but I can't be swayed."

"Too bad," she said. "These conventions are so dull. I thought we might be able to liven things up a little."

She moved back into the crowd, and Alex watched a number of his peers enjoy her graceful walk. Six months ago he might have taken Kathryn Ryan up on her invitation and enjoyed a few nights of passion.

However, last night with Larkin he had felt emotions he'd thought he would never experience again. She brought out in him a tenderness and optimism that made him feel he could conquer the world—or at least a part of it. The pleasures of the flesh were wonderful; but when the pleasures of the flesh were combined with love—well, that was something a man was willing to wait for.

Alex Jakobs was a man who knew his priorities.

LARKIN RETURNED from her business lunch around three o'clock that afternoon to find Patti, suffering jet lag but triumphant, waiting in her office.

"What are you doing here?" she asked, slipping out of her shoes and kicking them under her desk. "You're supposed to be in Palm Springs with Harry David Parker."

"Mission accomplished," Patti said. "He signed on the dotted line."

"Incredible! How did you manage it?"

Patti struck a campy, seductive pose. "Would you believe I used my feminine charms on him?"

"If I believed that, Franklin, you'd be on the unemployment line."

"You have no sense of humor, Larkin."

"You forget that your reputation precedes you." Larkin sat down behind her desk, and Patti took the seat adjacent to it.

"He wants the publicity for his novels, and the Learning Center seems to be as good a way as any for him to get some."

"Yes," Larkin said wryly, "and the several-thousand-dollar fee didn't hurt, either."

"He's a man of the arts," Patti said, popping a candy into her mouth. "Money means nothing to him."

Both women laughed at the absurdity of the statement. Over the years Larkin had discovered that those in the arts were the first to offer their services—for the right price.

"You're lucky Parker lives on the East End most of the year," Patti said, taking another candy. "Otherwise, I bet he'd expect you to pay all his expenses."

"That's one problem we shouldn't have with the ballet series, thank God."

Patti looked up from her inspection of her manicure "Did you get an answer from Karpo?"

"Karpov," Larkin corrected. "And yes, I did. A letter of agreement arrived this morning, by express mail."

Patti let out a whoop of excitement. "We can start publicizing?"

"Monday morning, if you like."

"The hell with Monday morning," Patti said. "I'll start right now."

Larkin laughed. "Remind me to talk to you about your lack of enthusiasm." She wished she felt one half the excitement Patti felt over Vladimir's association with the Learning Center. Her wariness was a strange counterpoint to Patti's elation.

"All we have to do is print a photo of that guy's body," Patti said, "and every woman on Long Island will be on line to sign up for the lecture series."

Vladimir's magnetic effect on women—and their effect on him—had been one of the main reasons Larkin ended their relationship. He was charmingly attractive and about as capable of being faithful as a tomcat on the prowl. Being second-best had been a painful experience, and Larkin vowed never to be second-best again.

So far, she had succeeded.

"I don't know how you ever let him slip through your fingers," Patti was saying. "The life you could have had—"

"Was highly overrated," Larkin broke in. "Don't believe everything you read about the glamorous life, Patti." There was nothing at all glamorous about a broken heart or shattered self-esteem.

"You take things too seriously."

"It wouldn't hurt you to do the same."

"I don't care what you say, Larkin. A man like Vladimir Karpov is worth five regular human beings."

Larkin sighed and shook her head. Patti might have known a lot of men, but she knew very little about life. Larkin's own experience with men was limited, but she knew that a smile from Alex was worth more than all the promises of "forever" from a man like Vladimir.

AT FIRST ALEX THOUGHT he was in the wrong building.

Even though the sign out front said The Learning Center, he was convinced that he had somehow made a wrong turn in the parking lot or gotten his days mixed up. He was certain their lunch date was for Monday, but the parking lot was jammed with cars, and yet there didn't seem to be a single living soul inside the school.

Now, he knew Larkin ran a series of odd classes that took people on leaf-peeping trips to New Hampshire and whale-watching jaunts to Cape Cod, but he had expected at least to find a receptionist in the office.

"Is anyone here?" His voice echoed in the quiet room.

He peeked into open classrooms stacked high with easels and stereo systems, woks and racquetball equipment. Still no sign of life anywhere. He was about to give up when he heard a woman's voice, low and melodic, counting slowly backward.

"Eight...seven...six...five..."

It came from the last room on the left. The door was slightly ajar, and he poked his head inside to take a look. There was Larkin, looking lovely in a cobalt-blue jump suit, stretched out on the floor along with thirty other women, while a woman with a yellow turban on her head counted backward.

He couldn't begin to hazard a guess.

Suddenly he heard a familiar voice next to him. "They're finishing a past-life regression."

He turned to see Patti Franklin, Larkin's assistant.

"That's Madame Sonia in the party hat," Patti continued. "She thinks she was Queen Hatshepsut in another life. The woman in the Harris Tweed suit was Alexander the Great, and the two women in Harvard sweatshirts were Nicholas and Alexandra."

"Which one was Czar Nicholas?"

"The one with the French braids. Can't you tell?"

"The accent had me fooled."

"We've had six Marie Antoinettes in the past two weeks," Patti continued. "We're thinking of giving out numbers."

"It wouldn't do to have two Marie Antoinettes in the same session, would it?" Alex couldn't help the chuckle in his voice.

"You think I'm joking, but we had two men come to blows—they both thought they were Humphrey Bogart."

This time Alex couldn't hold back his laughter. "I should set up a practice right here."

"Larkin would never go for that, but *I* think it's a great idea." Patti's enormous blue eyes sparkled at the prospect.

"I'm almost afraid to ask who Larkin was in her past life."

"There are days I'd swear she was Genghis Khan, but she'd probably say Joan of Arc."

Alex listened while the turbaned medium brought the class back to "this dimension of reality." One by one the women began to stretch, as if awakening from a long sleep.

He caught Larkin's eye, and she rose from the floor in one graceful motion and came toward him. Her extravagantly long hair was piled loosely on top of her head and big gold hoops dangled from her ears. Her smile was open and guileless, and in that instant he knew he had never seen a more beautiful woman in this life—or any other. The look she gave him set him on fire.

"Don't tell me," Patti said, "I already know. You were Joan of Arc."

Larkin shook her head and a long strand of hair fell across her shoulder. It took all of his self-control not to wrap its silky length around his hand.

"No, Franklin, I was Ivan the Terrible. Don't you have anything better to do than stand around smart-mouthing your employer?"

Patti gave Alex one of her patented come hither looks. "I wouldn't mind joining you and the good doctor for lunch."

"I don't recall inviting you along," Larkin said, winking at Alex.

Patti grinned. "A minor oversight. I have nothing against last-minute invitations, Larkin. Some of my best evenings were impromptu."

Alex was about to follow up on that intriguing statement when Larkin shook her head. "Don't encourage her, Alex. She already has a lunch date of her own."

"We could make it a foursome."

Alex laughed. "Another time, Patti."

Patti leered outrageously. "Another time I'd like it to be just the two of us."

"Don't you have some work to do?" Larkin asked.

Patti mumbled something about Larkin being Mussolini's second incarnation and disappeared down the hallway.

"So, tell me," Alex said as he and Larkin headed to her office to get her coat and shoes, "who were you in your past life?"

Larkin slipped into her spike-heel shoes and reached for her coat. "Would you believe a one-legged Swedish coal miner?"

"Not really." He held her bright red coat for her while she slid her arms into it. The scent of her perfume made him want to kick the door closed and pull her into his embrace. "Everyone else seemed to expect a royal past life."

"I'm afraid I was no exception." She unpinned her hair and let it flow over her collar and down her back. "I wanted to discover I'd lived the pampered life of a king's favorite lady, and instead I discover I was a one-legged coal miner— and a man, to boot! I didn't even have the good sense to be rich."

"Demand your money back," he said. "I've heard the management is quite reasonable."

"If I'd paid for that session, I would," Larkin said. "That was hardly the stuff of my romantic fantasies."

"You have elaborate fantasies?" *Dangerous question,* he thought. He only wanted an answer if he figured prominently in them.

"That's privileged information, wouldn't you say?" The look she gave him was so sexy that it nearly buckled his knees.

"You can tell me," he managed coolly, almost as if his body weren't on red alert. "I'm a doctor—I've heard it all before."

She perched on the edge of her desk while she fished through her pocketbook for something. "I've always had a yen for those old swashbuckler movies Tyrone Power and Errol Flynn made. I can't imagine anything more romantic than being stranded on a desert isle with a man in a billowy white shirt slashed down to there, tight pants and thigh-high black leather boots."

"Kinky, but within the bounds of reason."

"I'm glad you approve. I debated whether or not to mention the de rigueur gold-hoop earrings."

"What about the foul-mouthed parrot on his shoulder?"

She made a face. "Have you ever seen a pirate's shoulder after a parrot has been there? No, thanks. I can live without the wildlife."

"My fantasies are simpler," Alex said as they walked through the winding hallway back to the reception area. "A harem of voluptuous belly dancers would make me happy."

"I'm sure it would," Larkin said dryly. "You and every other man on earth."

He was enjoying the slight undercurrent of jealousy in her voice when they entered the lobby of the Center and came face-to-face with what seemed like enough long-stemmed American Beauty roses to cover three floats for the Rose Bowl on New Year's Day. Patti and a slender woman he didn't recognize stood in the center of the profusion of flowers.

"Are we giving a workshop on flower arranging and someone forgot to tell me?" Larkin gingerly stepped over a basket of fat red blossoms and looked at Patti.

Patti faked a loud sneeze. "If you have hay fever, you're in big trouble." She gestured around the room. "The delivery boy from Glo-Dot said there's a card, but when it comes to which basket it's in, your guess is as good as mine."

Alex saw a small white envelope poking out of a tall arrangement on the floor next to the receptionist's desk. Larkin's name was written diagonally across the front in slashing black letters.

"I found it." He handed Larkin the envelope.

She thanked him and pulled out a shiny white card.

"Come on!" Patti squealed. "Gestures like this are in the public domain. Who is it from?"

Larkin looked so uncomfortable that Alex almost wished she wouldn't say who the mysterious gift giver was, but his curiosity was gnawing away at his insides.

"Vladimir," she said finally, then tossed the card down on the desk. Patti's huge blue eyes seemed to be growing larger by the second. "Come on, Alex. Let's go to lunch."

Later on, Alex would wish he'd been able to control his curiosity, but on the way out he glanced down at the card on the desk. The words "Larkin, my love—29 November is too long to wait" instantly burned straight through his gut.

She was thirty years old, and he'd assumed she'd had her share of life's experiences. However, Alex hated it like hell that one of those experiences sent her a roomful of roses and was counting the days until November twenty-ninth.

Larkin was saying something to him as they crossed the parking lot to his rented car, and he tried to form an intelligent response. Unfortunately, there was but one coherent thought in his brain right then, and that one thought crowded out everything else.

Who the hell was Vladimir?

Chapter Nine

Amazing how something as innocuous as red roses could ruin an afternoon.

Vladimir's characteristically excessive gesture only amused Larkin, but if his scowl were any indication, it had sent Alex into a tailspin. Apparently even the most gifted of psychologists was not above the daily traumas of more ordinary mortals.

Twenty minutes later they were sitting in Steve's Pier 1 at one of the coveted tables with a breathtaking view of Long Island Sound. Unfortunately, they might as well have had a view of the parking lot for all the enjoyment the scenery was affording them.

Conversation had been limited to the weather and clams oreganato, and Larkin was now out of patience.

She pushed her white wine away from her and put her linen napkin on the table. Alex looked up from his salad.

"That's it," she said, picking up her handbag from the floor beside her chair. "I've exhausted every conversational gambit in my repertoire. I give up, Alex. I'm going to take a cab back to the school. Thanks for lunch."

She began to rise, praying that he would stop her.

"You haven't had lunch yet."

She met his eyes. "I've lost my appetite."

"Have I been that disagreeable?"

"You've been terrible."

"I apologize," he said. "Stay."

Her prayers were answered. "Will you tell me what's wrong?"

"I think you already know."

"The flowers?"

He nodded. "I thought I had evolved past jealousy like that. It took me by surprise."

Her only prior experience with jealousy had been one-sided: the sickening feeling in her stomach each time she heard rumors of Vladimir with another woman during their relationship.

"The flowers were from Vladimir Karpov." She waited for a glimmer of recognition but none came. "He defected from the Bolshoi Ballet five years ago. Do you remember that incident in the New York Public Library? The Russian embassy made a big to-do about it."

Alex nodded but said nothing.

"Vladimir is opening his own dance company and he'll be speaking at the Learning Center in November on the romance of ballet."

"There's more to it than that, isn't there?"

"Yes," she said. "We used to be lovers."

He flinched slightly. No one else would have noticed, but Larkin was so attuned to his discomfort that the slightest movement ricocheted through her own body.

"He'll be in New York in November to dance at Lincoln Center," she said. "Speaking at my school will give him plenty of free publicity and bring me a hell of a lot of new clients."

"You make it sound very cut-and-dried."

She couldn't help but notice a flicker of relief on Alex's face. "It is," she said, suddenly not all that certain she was telling the truth. "We've managed to stay friendly. This is a mutually advantageous business deal. Nothing more."

It would be easy to say that, while the love was long over, friendship remained, but that merely scratched the surface of a very complex truth: she couldn't wait for Vladimir to see the woman she had become. In her success, she wanted him to realize all he'd lost when she walked out the door.

Alex remained silent. A waitress in black pants and a white tuxedo shirt deposited their lunch in front of them and discreetly hurried away.

Larkin shifted in her seat. If Alex didn't say something in the next five seconds, she was going to tip the entire dish of sole meunière onto the lap of his expensive Italian suit.

Finally he looked up. "You've told me more than I have any right to know, Larkin. Thank you."

She watched him intently. "I didn't know any other way to approach this, Alex." She did, however, withhold the pain she'd felt over Vladimir's infidelities and the long struggle she'd had to recover her balance.

At least you know what you're up against, she thought as his gray eyes met hers. She and Vladimir had come to a normal parting of the ways. Alex and Rikki had been tragically torn apart.

She would much rather be able to see her competition face-to-face than have to live up to a memory.

Real people had faults.

Memories rarely had any at all.

ALEX WOULD HAVE GIVEN anything to begin that afternoon all over again.

They were sitting at a table for two, but the shadows of Vladimir and Rikki were so real that he was tempted to pull up two more chairs and invite them to sit down.

How much easier it was to love when you were young—when experience was limited and expectations still ran high. How much safer it was to give your heart to someone when you still believed in forever.

What he wanted was the impossible: to keep his memories of Rikki alive and to wipe Karpov out of Larkin's heart forever.

Sexist. Unfair. Impossible.

But so damnably human that he couldn't resist a laugh of defeat. Her enormous green eyes were shadowed with caution as she looked at him.

"You realize I want the impossible, don't you?" he asked.

"Don't we all?" A smile played at the edges of her mouth. "Why should you be any different?"

"Because I was trained to believe I was," he said. "I'm supposed to solve these problems, not get caught up in them."

"You're only human, Alex." Her voice was tender, unbearably so.

"So I'm learning."

Larkin toyed with the spoon in her coffee cup. "I feel at a disadvantage," she said slowly. "I know very little about you beyond the fact that you're a psychologist and that you lost your wife."

And so he told her about his parentless childhood and the foster homes in the Bronx and Brooklyn. He told her about Rikki and the way she brought a boy of thirteen to life with her unquestioning love. He told her about the struggle through City College, about endless work and endless love.

"We'd really made it," he said over his fourth cup of coffee. Larkin was still watching him, eyes glistening. "The student loans were paid off; I'd established a practice. Rikki was able to quit work and we were going to start a family." He had to clear his throat before he could continue. "Only problem was, starting a family was the one thing we didn't seem able to do."

The joke between them had been: start a family or take flying lessons. Of course, it had never really been a contest—he wanted a child as much as she did. The private pilot's license and the Cessna 207 would be next.

"They kept saying to relax, take it easy, take a vacation. It'll happen. When it did, we felt as if we had discovered a new universe. Unfortunately, Rikki miscarried in her third month, and a routine D and C turned up a very nonroutine, invasive cancer. Ten months later she was dead."

Tears slid down Larkin's cheeks, and she reached over to take his hand.

"It's ironic," he said, linking his fingers with hers. "The best part of my life is spent in the cockpit of that damned Cessna, and I would trade it in a second if it would bring Rikki back."

Larkin didn't say anything at all, simply held his hand and shared his pain.

It was a hell of a thing to talk about with the woman he was wooing, but she had wanted to know, and she deserved the truth. He couldn't minimize what he'd shared with Rikki to maximize what he wanted to share with Larkin. Both women deserved better treatment than that, even if it meant romance took a back seat to reality for the moment.

If what they had together was the real thing, the romance would take care of itself when the time was right. Of that he had no doubt.

LARKIN FELT HER EMOTIONS closing in on her. *You asked for it, Walker. You wanted to know all about him.*

She watched as Alex maneuvered the car onto Sagtikos State Parkway and headed south back to the school. Their long, surprisingly intimate lunch had taken them beyond the need for small talk.

Alex had popped a cassette of The Temptations into the tape player and he was humming along to "My Girl" in a slightly off-key bass that made her smile. He seemed to have lost some of that aura of sadness that she had noticed the first time they met, and for that Larkin was grateful.

However, knowing he had been married and lost his wife was vastly different from knowing he had loved a woman named Rikki who had adored him since eighth grade—a woman who had provided him with the only stable family life he had ever known.

It was a tough act to follow.

Twenty minutes later they pulled into the parking lot at the Center and Alex pulled in next to her red Datsun.

"It went longer than I thought," he said, helping her out of the low-slung sports car he'd rented. "I hope it didn't cause you any problems."

She smiled. "That's one of the great things about being the boss. I don't have to explain myself to anyone."

The parking lot was empty, except for Patti's and Sharon's cars over near the fence. Alex leaned against the side of the sports car and pulled Larkin into his arms.

"This was hardly the romantic interlude I'd envisioned," he said, stroking her hair. "I'm sorry."

His touch made it difficult to think clearly. "Don't be," she managed. "We had to talk about these things sometime, didn't we?"

"I'd hoped we could postpone that until later in our relationship."

So had she. "I should be getting in, Alex. I teach a tap-dancing class at four-thirty."

"Sounds interesting. Suppose I could audit a session some day?"

She grinned. "You name the day. I'll expect you in white tie and tails."

"You teach Fred Astaire routines?"

"Of course," she said. "We're a first-class establishment."

The banter was light and easy, but she couldn't quite shake the odd emotions the afternoon had stirred up inside her.

"Dinner Wednesday?" He brushed a kiss along the side of her jaw.

She shook her head. "I'm moderating a panel that night. Thursday?"

"My *Helpline* taping. We're doing a live show and putting three more in the can."

"Our schedules seem to be incompatible," she said. "Is there any hope for us?" The statement was meant to sound ironic and witty. Unfortunately, it came out sounding exactly the way she felt—melancholy.

"I'll call you tonight," he said. "We'll compare calendars. It'll work out, Larkin. I promise."

She would have believed him twenty-four hours ago. Now she wasn't sure about anything.

At least, she wasn't sure until he put his hand gently beneath her chin and raised her face for his kiss. Desire rose within her but was overshadowed by an intense sweetness that took her by surprise.

The sound of an unmuffled engine broke the spell they were under. Larkin looked up to see Gordon parking his Chevy near his sister's car. He cut the engine and got out. He still hadn't looked their way.

"How's your cold, Gordon?" Larkin called out. "You should have stayed out another day."

He stopped about twenty feet away from Larkin and Alex. "It's okay," he mumbled. "Patti said the roof needs more work." He looked at Alex when he spoke.

"Well, don't overdo," Larkin said. She noticed his color seemed unusually high. "We need you too much to have you getting sick again."

She was about to introduce him to Alex when he turned abruptly and went into the school.

"He's so shy." Larkin looked up at Alex. "He doesn't mean to be rude."

"You're wrong," Alex said. "He meant it."

"Why would he be rude to me? We've never had any problems."

"He wasn't being rude to you, Larkin. That was directed toward me."

"I don't understand."

"Don't you?" Alex asked. "It's pretty obvious he's infatuated with you."

She could feel her cheeks reddening. "I know he's grateful for the job, but—"

Alex kissed her again. "Being grateful is one thing, Larkin. What I'm talking about is something else again."

"He's Patti's brother, Alex. I hardly think I have to worry."

Alex seemed unconvinced, but he let the subject drop. Could he possibly be jealous of someone as young and callow as Gordon Franklin? What a delightful thought.

He walked her to the door and they kissed one more time. Alex again promised to call her later that night. He still seemed a little disturbed by Gordon's behavior.

"Gordon is just a sweet kid with a few problems," she said, touching Alex's lips with the tip of her index finger. "There's nothing to worry about. Now let me get back to work."

ALEX COULDN'T GET Gordon out of his thoughts.

There's nothing to worry about. Larkin was probably right. Why in hell was he getting so rattled by a young man with a case of unrequited love?

Alex pushed aside the galleys of his *Metro Monthly* article on the singles' seminar and rubbed his eyes. For hours now, he had been unable to get Gordon Franklin out of his mind. There had been something about the expression in Gordon's eyes as he looked at him, an intensity that seemed excessive for the situation. It wasn't hard to understand the jealousy Gordon might have felt seeing Larkin in his arms, but the look of anger on his young face had gotten beneath Alex's skin.

You're making too much of it, he thought, lighting a cigarette. Infatuation. That's all it was. The kid was head over heels for Larkin. Who could blame him for having his gut twist when he saw her in the arms of another man?

All Alex had to do was think about the red roses in Larkin's office and the card written in Karpov's sprawling hand to understand everything Gordon Franklin was feeling.

Alex only hoped he handled himself half as well when he came face-to-face with his own rival.

IT TOOK PATTI until six o'clock to find spots for all the roses. Larkin had just finished her tap class and was resting on the sofa in her office, sipping a Diet Coke. Rose petals were scattered all over the carpet, tabletops and file cabinets.

"Well, now I know where this came from," Larkin said, fingering the ballet charm she'd received a few weeks ago. "Vladimir."

Patti gazed around at the flower-filled room. "It kind of makes you wonder what he's going to send next."

Larkin suddenly made up her mind. She unclasped the fine gold chain and handed it to Patti. "Here," she said, "with my best regards."

"Are you crazy?" Patti said, looking at the beautifully crafted necklace. "It's yours."

Larkin shook her head. "Not anymore." She didn't need or want any tacit agreements with Vladimir that went beyond speaking at the Center. "Enjoy."

"I will," Patti said, putting the necklace on. "Does this mean I get Karpov, too?"

"He's an extremely charming man, Patti, but you'll only end up with a broken heart."

Patti shrugged. "I've had my heart broken by lesser men," she said. "Why not have my heart broken by the best?"

Larkin sighed. "Be careful what you wish for, Patti. You just might get it."

"Don't worry about me," Patti said, opening a soda. "I can take care of myself."

Larkin nodded. She wished she could say the same. For hours now, she'd found herself wondering about Erika Lewin Jakobs, the woman Alex had loved and married—and lost. Her beginner dance students had done a simple tap routine with more flair and precision than she, a fact that had generated a bit of good-natured teasing. They had assumed love was the reason for her silly mistakes, and she hadn't discouraged that.

In a way, love *was* to blame.

She had played second fiddle to Vladimir's career; she'd played second fiddle to more "other women" than she cared to think about.

But this time, with Alex Jakobs, she'd rather not get involved if it meant playing second fiddle to a woman who existed only in his heart. She wasn't sure that she could bounce back quite so easily this time.

Across the room Patti groaned. "What I wouldn't give for a pizza right now." She looked at Larkin. "Can I convince you to share one with me?"

"I'm not that hungry, Patti. Ask Gordon. Maybe he'd split it with you."

Patti buzzed Gordon in the storeroom, and a few seconds later he appeared in the doorway. He looked over at Larkin. "Yes?"

"Not me this time," she said, smiling at him. "Your sister wants to know if you're in the mood for a pepperoni with extra cheese."

His gaze lingered on her for a second; then he turned to Patti. "I suppose you want me to pick it up, don't you?"

Patti grinned. "And one more Diet Coke."

"Make it two," Larkin said. "I should have known I couldn't resist."

Gordon turned to her again. This time his face had the peculiar look of one who'd just awakened from a long and restless sleep. Larkin suddenly felt uncomfortable, and she pushed Alex's words from her mind. "Is my mascara smudged?" she asked lightly.

He shook his head and averted his eyes once again. "Do you want me to go to Lorenzo's and get it?" he asked Patti.

"You don't mind, do you, Gord? I have to be here when the tarot card class comes in to register." She fiddled with the ballet-shoes charm that glittered around her neck. Gordon's eyes suddenly seemed riveted to it.

"Where did that come from?"

Patti winked at Larkin. "I haven't wanted it to leak out to the press, brother dear, but Vladimir Karpov and I are an item."

Gordon didn't smile or laugh or do any of the things Larkin might have expected him to do.

"Where did you get it, Patti?"

Larkin sat up straighter on the couch. A peculiar buzzing tension raced through her body.

"You don't believe me, little brother?" Patti asked. Larkin detected annoyance cloaked inside the light tone of Patti's voice. "I'm highly insulted."

"Don't make a fool out of me, Patti," he said. "You don't even know Karpov."

Patti laughed. Larkin had the distinct feeling that her assistant was carrying the charade too far. "There's a lot you don't know about me, brother mine," she said airily. "Karpov and I have been intimate for years."

This time Gordon said nothing at all. He just turned around and left. Seconds later they heard the sound of the back door slamming shut.

"What in hell was the matter with him?" Patti shook her head in amazement. "Can't he take a joke?"

"Apparently not," Larkin said. "Maybe you should go a little easier on him, Patti."

Patti looked down at the charm around her neck and sighed. "If it wasn't so absurd, I'd almost think he was jealous."

An involuntary shiver raced through Larkin. "It almost seemed that way, didn't it?" she mused. She had been so busy dwelling on Rikki Jakobs that Alex's warning had completely slipped her mind. Could there be more to his suspicions than simple garden-variety jealousy? "Has Gordon said anything to you lately?"

Patti made a face. "Gordon is as silent as the grave," she said as they heard the roar of his Chevy's engine starting up. "He keeps everything bottled up inside him. Why do you think he had so much trouble after our folks died?"

Sorrow did strange things to people, Larkin knew. Losing her parents had set Patti Franklin off on an endless quest for love. Patti, however, was the first to admit her problem. Larkin wondered what it was that Gordon was seeking.

The old Chevy barreled down the driveway and screeched out into the traffic on Main Street. "Do you think he'll be all right?" Larkin asked.

Patti looked at her and smiled. "Of course he'll be all right," she said. "I just hope he remembers to get the Diet Cokes."

HE HADN'T MADE himself clear enough.

The shadows had been his home for so long that what seemed so clear to him was obscured for everyone else.

He had thought his gesture both romantic and obvious, and the sight of it against her skin had been almost as good as the touch of her mouth against his.

He could still see her in that man's arms, her slender body pulled up against him until she couldn't break away. He would never forget that split second of panic on her lovely face when the man claimed her mouth with his.

It would never be like that with him. He understood kindness and tenderness. A woman like that was too special to maul in a parking lot as if she were some cheap whore.

Maybe the car hadn't been warning enough.

Maybe he would have to step out of the shadows long enough to make very sure his message was understood.

He didn't want to wait forever for her.

Chapter Ten

There was no denying the fact that Alex and Larkin had reached a turning point, but unfortunately, that turning point seemed to lead away from their growing relationship.

Two long late-night phone calls and one splendid evening of dinner and dancing had failed to bridge the gap, and Alex was beginning to feel that Roger Lacey's costume party just might mean the end of his relationship with Larkin—whatever that relationship might be.

A few days before the party he turned to Judy Lincoln for consolation and advice.

"I can't believe it," Judy said over coffee in her kitchen. "Alex Jakobs, famous psychologist, comes to a lowly mathematician for advice." She slipped her hand inside her blouse and made it flutter with her fingers. "Be still, my heart."

"Cut it out, Judy," Alex said, grabbing another onion bagel and loading it with cream cheese. "I need a woman's opinion."

"About a patient?"

"About me."

"Is there a woman, Alex?"

"Yes."

"Serious?" Judy's eyes twinkled.

"Would I have flown down here in the middle of the week if it weren't?"

"I thought my western omelet might have been the attraction."

"Not this time, Jude." He told her about Larkin, about the intense attraction he felt toward her.

Judy polished off the rest of her hash browns. "Terrific," she said, looking up at him. "What's the problem?"

This was the tough part. "It's hard to explain."

Judy raised an eyebrow. "Come on, Alex. We've known each other way too long for this."

He dragged his hand through his hair, an old nervous gesture of his. "Lately I find myself thinking about Rikki all the time," he said quietly. The dreams had been coming every night, haunting him. "I know it's irrational, but I feel guilty as all hell."

"You know better than that, Alex. Phil would say—"

"Phil would say exactly what I would say. I don't want a professional opinion, Judy, I want a personal one."

Old friends had certain privileges, and Judy took advantage of one of them. "I don't think you're feeling guilty, Jakobs. I think you're feeling scared."

He winced. "Whatever happened to beating around the bush?"

"Is that what you wanted me to do?"

He shook his head, and Judy grinned.

"I didn't think so," she said.

"This is all new to me. The last time I felt like this I was thirteen years old and the victim of raging hormones."

"Are you in love with Larkin Walker?"

He took his time before he answered, weighing carefully all the things besides chemistry that drew him to her. "Ten days ago I would have said yes. Now it seems as if we've taken one giant step backward."

"Does she know you were married?"

"I told Larkin all about Rikki."

"Maybe she's feeling a bit intimidated, Alex. What you and Rikki shared spanned a lot of years."

"I don't think the problem's with Larkin," he said. There was no point in evading the issue any longer. "I think the problem's mine." He told Judy about the shower of red roses Larkin received from Vladimir Karpov and his own decidedly adolescent response to them. "I want Larkin to accept the fact I've loved before, but when I see proof she's loved some other man, I turn into a jealous fool."

"Don't be so hard on yourself. Who wouldn't be a bit put off by someone like Karpov?"

"You've heard of him?"

"What rock have you been lying under?"

"You know I'm not a balletomane."

"You don't have to like ballet to be aware of Karpov," Judy said. "He was front-page news when he defected to the United States in the reading room of the New York Public Library. I think another dancer helped shelter him and—" She stopped and stared at Alex. "My God! Larkin?"

Alex nodded. "One and the same."

"I think I understand how you're feeling. Karpov is probably the most charismatic, sexy man who ever—"

He raised his hand. "Spare me the details. I think I get the general drift, Judy."

Judy made a show of looking him over. "You're not exactly a slouch in the looks department either, Jakobs. If I didn't have Phil, I just might give Ms Walker a run for her money."

"You're too kind," he said dryly. "I'm a moody, intense psychologist, not a jet-setter dancer."

"She's not with that jet-setter dancer anymore, is she?" Judy got up to toast another bagel. Alex wondered how she managed to stay so slim when she ate like a starving truck driver. "He may be gorgeous, but something obviously was lacking. If the gossip rags are correct, he's second in line only to Warren Beatty in the one-night-stand department."

"You can't believe everything you read, Judy."

"Well, I don't see the problem. You're brilliant, handsome and loyal. What more could she want?"

"Excitement," he said. "A touch of fantasy. We've only known each other a few weeks, and already we're bogged down in reality."

"You want to start over again with Larkin, right? You want to sweep her off her feet and make her forget Karpov ever existed."

"You're a smart woman, Jude. Have you ever thought of becoming a therapist?"

"Heaven forbid! I'm the sane one in this family." She gave him the same smile he'd seen her bestow on Tommy and Cameron. "It seems to me you have the perfect opportunity right under your all-too-literal nose."

Alex knew he must have an idiotic expression on his face, but he couldn't help it. He had no idea what Judy was talking about.

She sighed. "Alex, Alex, what am I going to do with you? Don't you know anything about costume parties?"

"I know they're a chance for grown men and women to make utter fools of themselves by dressing up as Cabbage Patch Kids and Mr. T. Beyond that, I can't see where Lacey's party means anything more than that."

"How little you know about life," Judy said. "Sit back, Alex, and I'll tell you all about the erotic possibilities inherent in a costume party. I think you'll be surprised."

He was.

And Larkin would be even more surprised when she saw him.

ROGER WAS MODELING his costume for his Halloween party four days from now, and Larkin found it difficult to muster the requisite amount of enthusiasm.

"Really, darling," he said as he slipped out of his feather boa, "the least you could do is feign polite interest."

"I'm sorry. I guess my mind is elsewhere."

"Dare I hazard a guess? You're thinking about Dr. J."

"Am I that obvious?"

"Sometimes." He sat down next to her on his sleek black sofa. "Feel like talking about it? I've been told I'm a first-rate listener."

Roger Lacey could make her laugh, and there were times when his sarcastic wit could make her furious, but when Larkin needed him, he was always there for her. This time was no exception.

"Is the road to romance a bit rocky these days?

She shook her head. "I wish it were that simple."

"Things are going well?"

"I don't really know. When I'm with Alex everything is fine—wonderful, actually." She paused, searching for the right way to explain the emotions that had been keeping her up late the past two weeks. "It's when we're apart that the doubts start creeping in."

Roger motioned toward the copy of *People* magazine on her coffee table. Vladimir Karpov's face smiled up at them in all its Slavic splendor. "Are you beginning to yearn for the Blond Bombshell?"

Vladimir was a physically splendid man, and she would be a liar if she said some of her memories didn't still make her knees grow slightly rubbery. However, she also remembered why their relationship had ended—and how long it had taken her to recover her self-respect.

No, she wasn't likely to make that mistake a second time.

"It's not my past love I'm worried about, Roger," she said finally. "It's his."

Roger grinned wickedly. "Has some raven-haired beauty from his deep, dark past slithered back into town?"

"A redhead," she said. "Rikki was a redhead."

"No competition. Redheads freckle in the sun."

She couldn't help but laugh at this absurd statement. "A perfect tan is the gateway to happiness?"

"That and a perfect body."

"I'm being serious, Roger."

He took her hand and squeezed it. "I'm trying, Larkin, but it's tough to stay serious when you're wearing a padded bra."

She reached inside his sequined gown and pulled out the pair of falsies. She tossed them behind the couch. "There. Now you have no excuse."

"So tell me about this Rikki you're so worried about. Were they together a long time? Are you afraid they're still seeing each other?"

"They were together about eighteen years."

Roger whistled low. "High school sweethearts?"

She nodded. "They married when he was just eighteen."

"And you think he's still carrying a torch for her?"

She felt a distinct pain in her chest. "It's a possibility."

"Well, where's your fire, girl? I've never known you to take a back seat to anyone, Larkin."

"It's not that simple."

"You've said that before." He slipped a denim work shirt over his strapless gown. "They're not together anymore, are they?" he asked. "That counts for something. Possession *is* nine-tenths of the law."

"They didn't break up, Roger," she said. "Rikki died."

His grin faded. "That changes things, doesn't it?"

"More than you know." She told Roger much of what Alex had told her, being careful to withhold the more intimate details in deference to Alex's personal privacy. "They were totally involved with each other—one of those relationships where you can't tell where one ends and the other begins."

Even the normally cynical Roger Lacey seemed moved by what she chose to tell him. "The type of relationship we're all looking for?"

She nodded.

"That's a tough act to follow, kid."

"I know." She didn't need Roger to confirm her fears. "You were supposed to tell me not to worry."

"Don't worry."

"You don't sound very convincing."

"Sorry," he said, "but I can't play fairy godmother and wave a magic wand to make it all come out okay."

"That was a terrible choice of metaphor," she said, suppressing a chuckle, "but I understand what you're trying to say."

"What was she like?" Roger poured them each a glass of wine. "Working woman? Doctor? Lawyer? Indian chief? Mother of three?"

"She was Alex's wife," Larkin said slowly. "She taught school for a while, but primarily she was Alex's wife."

"An old-fashioned marriage?"

Larkin nodded. The parallel between her parents' marriage and the Jakobses' was not lost on her.

"Are you jealous of what she had with him?"

Leave it to Roger to zero in on the heart of the matter. "A little."

"This is me you're talking to, Larkin."

"All right." She grinned. "A lot. I know it's ridiculous to feel this way, but there it is. I just can't help it. I want to see pictures of her. I wonder about the sound of her voice. She was everything to him, and I don't know if I could ever give myself to a man in quite that way again."

"Has our good doctor asked you to marry him, then?"

"No."

"Have you shared—how shall I say it—physical pleasure with each other?"

"You're getting a little personal, Roger."

"I'll take that righteous indignation to mean no." He leaned forward and took her hand. "So what's the problem, then, darling? Enjoy what you have and don't ask questions. Life is serious enough. Don't look for trouble.''

"I wish it were that easy."

"But it *is* that easy, darling. All you have to do is weave a little bit of fantasy around the two of you and put reality on hold for a while."

"Don't go getting strange on me, Roger."

He scowled. "You have a filthy mind. What I'm talking about even Ron and Nancy would approve of."

"I come to you for advice and I get riddles instead."

"How can you claim to hail from Las Vegas and know so little about fantasy? Where's your creative imagination, Walker?"

"I don't have any," she said, grinning. "The Learning Center hasn't gotten around to it yet."

"Don't you see?" He was practically shouting at her. "My Halloween party is the perfect time for you and Dr. J. to create a few new fantasies of your own."

"You've lost me, Roger. I don't see what your pagan ritual has to do with anything."

"You're beyond redemption, Walker. Maybe it's time you forgot about his wife and your ex-beau—" he glanced down at the magazine cover and sighed melodramatically "—and started over again."

There was a certain charm to his idea. "And you think wearing a costume will help?"

"As long as it's not a tutu."

"I don't think Alex would wear a tutu."

"More's the pity," Roger shot back. "It's you I won't let in the door in one."

She gave him a wicked grin. "I've been thinking of coming as Shirley Temple. My tap shoes are—"

Roger lunged for her throat. "Do I have to teach you everything? Think seduction! Think sex! Think—"

"Concubine?"

"That's the spirit!"

"A harem dancer?"

"A little clichéd, perhaps, but you've got the idea."

"I can see it now," she said, beginning to catch his enthusiasm. "Veils, jewels in the navel, the mysterious lure of the East..."

Hadn't Alex himself mentioned a harem girl as one of his prime fantasies? She bubbled over with ideas.

"Whose fantasy is this?" Roger asked finally. "You're supposed to concentrate on fulfilling *his* fantasies, not yours, Larkin."

She gave her friend a quick hug. "That's where you're wrong, Roger."

Creating this fantasy world for Alex was something she was doing all for herself.

THE TRANSITION from sedate psychologist to swashbuckling pirate had been easier than Alex cared to admit. The second he donned those tight-fitting pants and thigh-high boots in the privacy of the dressing room at Calley's Costumes on Jericho Turnpike, he was hooked.

Okay, so he had a few shaky moments on the way to Roger's when he stopped for gas and three young women in a Trans Am made some pointed suggestions about his sword but, all in all, this whole idea seemed to be working.

It was hard to be Alex Jakobs, Ph.D., when you were wearing a white silk shirt cut down to the navel and a gold hoop earring.

He parked his car in Larkin's driveway, secured his mask, and walked over to Roger's yard, where fluorescent orange balloons bobbed from the bare branches of the oak trees and an enormous ghost in designer sheets menaced the flagstone path. Larkin had told him to meet her at the party because she would be helping Roger set things up. The door was open and he went inside, where Dolly Parton, in a beaded red gown, gave him an outrageous wink.

"Glad you could make it, honey," Dolly said, sounding a hell of a lot like Roger Lacey. "Hang your sword in the closet and join the party!" Dolly waved in the general direction of the music and tottered away on her red wedgies with her backfield in motion.

The scene in the enormous living room was a cross between Walt-Disney-meets-Federico-Fellini and *Gone with the Wind*, and Alex felt uncomfortable until he remembered that he was no longer a respected psychologist but the villainous Alex the Blackhearted, whose goal in life was to pillage and hijack and wench.

Scarlett O'Hara swirled by in a cloud of perfume. For a second, Alex thought she was Larkin, but quickly he saw she lacked Larkin's grace and line.

A tall blonde dressed as an eighteenth-century tavern wench sidled up to him. "Aye, ye're a fine laddie," she said. "Where would ye be stayin' the night?"

Obviously there was a whole new world of role-playing out there that his colleagues knew nothing about.

"*The Merry Widow* is in port, lass, and I with her," he said, calling upon his memory of old Errol Flynn movies. "And she's a fine ship, she is." He could almost swear he felt the salt air against his face; then he remembered Roger's home was on the water.

She was a fine wench, but he excused himself, saying he had to seek out his first mate. He elbowed past three more Scarlett O'Haras, two geriatric Cabbage Patch Kids, and a formidable Cleopatra. The party overflowed from the living room into the dining alcove and points east, and he searched the crowd for Larkin, but she was nowhere to be found.

He slipped out the back door and was about to cross the moon-swept yard toward Larkin's house when he heard a soft rustle from the deck that overlooked Great South Bay.

Her long amber hair swirled around her delicate face as she turned and looked at him. Wisps of diaphanous cloth shot through with silver and gold covered what was essential and promised everything else. She met his eyes and smiled at him, and he felt as if he were spontaneously combusting right there in the middle of Roger's Halloween party.

She was every moonlight fantasy he'd ever had, every dream he'd ever entertained in the darkness. But she was real, and he knew beyond doubt that she would be his tonight.

HE WAS THE MOST GLORIOUS male apparition Larkin had ever seen.

Even her wildest leap of imagination would have fallen far short of the reality of Alex as he walked toward where she stood on the redwood deck. Why on earth had she ever thought things were cooling between them? The fever in her blood burned hot and fierce as he moved closer to where she waited for him.

The golden hoop in his ear glittered in the moonlight. "I like your earring."

His dark gray eyes traveled her body, then lingered at her navel. "I like your emerald."

She glanced down at the enormous fake jewel in her belly button. "It's cold and it's uncomfortable," she said. "It took two tubes of eyelash glue to make it stick."

The look in his eyes made her tremble with excitement. "You have to admit it's effective," he said.

She gave a little shimmy and the glittering veils brushed gently against his arm. "Glad you like it."

"I do." His white teeth flashed against his dark beard as he smiled. "Very much." He moved away from her and brandished his sword with a flourish. "What do you think of Alex the Blackhearted?"

I think you're the most exciting man I've ever seen. "Have you been studying old Errol Flynn movies? You look as if you were born to the piratical life." He looked reckless and hungry and more than a little dangerous.

"You'll dance for me later." It was a command, not a request.

The sound of his voice made her tremble with longing.

"I'll dance for you now," she said. They had moved away from the noise and lights of the house, and in the moonlit darkness she began to sway, her torso and hips beckoning him with age-old promises of delight. Alex leaned against a silvery willow tree. His arms were folded across his chest, and his lean hard muscles rippled against his silky shirt. His mask dangled from one finger.

In her mind were Beledi rhythms, which she recreated with the zills, the tiny cymbals held between her fingers. The sheer skirts helped hide her legs and the hard work the dance entailed; all that showed was sinuous, enticing movement, movement meant to invite even as it kept her just beyond reach.

A stiff wind blew up from Great South Bay and whipped her hair around her face, tangling it in the filmy costume. She felt as wild and free as the wind, as if the untamed weather matched something equally untamed inside her soul. She had chosen not to wear the heavy belt of gold coins; instead, a delicate necklace of tiny silver bells rested between her breasts, adding its music to the sound of the wind and the water and the pounding of her heart.

Alex's eyes never left hers as she danced, her hips lifting higher and higher to the rhythm inside her, her arms tracing graceful patterns in the night. She was acutely aware of the sway of her breasts, the feel of the October air against her bare skin, the weight of her hair as it moved with her. She was filled with a female power, an inexplicable pagan sense of strength that radiated from her and heightened every movement she made with a sensuality she never knew she was capable of experiencing.

Suddenly Alex moved closer. With the tip of his sword he gently drew one layer of her shimmering costume away from her body, then another layer and another. She stopped dancing and stood, legs apart, breasts heaving, her breath coming hard and fast.

"I feel as if I don't even know you," she whispered.

"You *don't* know me," he said, drawing closer. "Tonight you don't know me at all. Tonight everything is new."

She shivered with pleasure. "You sound like a dangerous man."

"Around you, I am."

She leaned her head against his chest; his flesh burned against her cheek. His scent made a luscious hunger rise up inside her body. His powerful hands slid down over the curve of her back and cupped her rounded buttocks, pulling her up against his own rising excitement.

A sound began to form in the back of her throat— whether a gasp of pleasure or surprise she would never know because he swept her into his arms and, without a word, carried her across the wide and silent yard to her house.

Chapter Eleven

Larkin had left a light burning in the hallway, so it was easy for Alex to find the bedroom. Magic and illusion were so much a part of the moment that he would have hated to ask for anything as mundane as directions to her room.

"Alex?" Larkin's voice was a husky whisper as he put her down near the bed.

He spotted a Victorian brass candle holder on her night table. She handed him matches from the drawer, and a second later the flame cast their shadows against the wall. He ripped the white shirt off his body and tossed it to the floor. She reached behind her, and layers of gossamer drifted to the carpet. He went to pull her toward him, but she eluded him, a small smile playing at the corners of her mouth.

She began to sway once more to some internal rhythm. The bottom part of her harem costume dipped low across her pelvis, accentuating the womanly curves of her body. The chain of tiny silver bells nestled between her breasts, its sound lost against the pounding of his blood. Through the long, sheer skirt he could see the parting of her thighs. His mind turned to flame.

He knelt before her and ripped the skirt from her body with his teeth. Her gasp of surprise became a moan of pleasure as he ran his tongue lightly across her abdomen. The flesh was firm, and it quivered at his touch. Her hands fumbled with the zipper on his tight black pants, and he gently pushed her away and stripped off his boots and trousers.

She watched every movement he made, those beautiful green eyes of hers caressing the muscles of his thighs, the line of his torso, the throbbing desire between his legs. His looks had never meant anything to him before; now he gloried in his ability to excite her as she had excited him.

And then she came to him and they fell to the bed, and everything he'd ever known about making love proved a poor, poor substitute for what he found in the arms of Larkin Walker.

"YOU ARE DANGEROUS," Larkin whispered. "You're a dangerous man."

She lay atop him, her breasts grazing his muscular chest, her breathing still harsh and ragged from their fierce coupling of a few moments ago. The sheer male force of his passion had torn away her reserve, much as he had torn away the filmy costume shielding her body.

It had taken nothing more than the sight of him, nude and gloriously aroused, to send her crashing over the edge of reason. How easy—how terrifyingly easy—it was to disappear before a force as irresistible as desire.

And how easy it was to glory in this simple act made complicated by the power of the human heart.

Alex's large hands spanned her waist, then lifted her, repositioning them so that she lay beneath his body. His mouth found hers as he moved slowly within her. For an instant, she wanted to stop, to pull back from madness, but then he whispered her name and gladly she stepped over the edge.

THE HALLOWEEN PARTY was long since over, but the gray Buick was still parked in her driveway.

He knew it belonged to the dark-haired man, for he'd memorized the license plate weeks ago. Funny how the damage no longer showed.

He'd listened by the window for the sound of her voice. If she'd cried out, he would have smashed through the glass to save her. But there had been no sound at all, and the pain in his gut grew sharp and strong.

Red-hot images of her tangled in the arms of the dark-haired man brought bile to his throat and he fought down the urge to vomit.

Early sunlight washed over the spot where he hid. He was still cold, and he turned up the collar on his leather jacket.

It was almost time to come out from the shadows.

INSTEAD OF AWAKENING in Alex's arms, eager for him, Larkin found herself leaving the warm bed not long after dawn. She showered and dressed, then went in to prepare breakfast, seeking some time and space for herself.

Her body still tingled from their passion of the previous night; she would never forget those first shattering moments when there was nothing in the world but pleasure. Total surrender was something she equated with the young girl she once had been, and the fact that she lost control so completely with Alex last night made her question her hard-won independence.

The shower in the master bathroom clanked on. Last night she had wanted to curl inside his heart and stay there forever. This morning the house seemed too small to contain the two of them and all they brought into the relationship.

She had found it easier to share her body with him the night before than she was finding it to share her home with him that morning. An unpleasant fact, but true, nevertheless.

She was dipping thick slices of challah into batter for French toast when Alex appeared, barefoot and in his pirate costume, in the doorway.

"This isn't quite as effective in the daylight, is it?" His thick chestnut hair was damp and it fell over his forehead in a very attractive manner. Larkin wished he would comb it back.

"You need the boots," she said. "Pirates never go barefoot. It's not good for the image." She put two slices of bread on the griddle and they sizzled.

"I thought the sword was supposed to be the focal point."

She shook her head, pushing aside bawdier images. "It's the boots," she said, turning the French toast so it could brown on the other side. She wished he had his boots on because she couldn't remember the last time she'd washed the kitchen floor.

He pushed his damp hair off his face.

"There's a blow dryer in the guest bathroom."

"I don't use blow dryers," he said. "Never got the hang of them."

He walked barefoot to the kitchen table. His white silk shirt, slashed to the waist, looked incongruous at her suburban breakfast table. He was probably the only pirate in existence who carried a beeper.

She realized that there was a definite need for a course on "Dealing with the Morning After." She'd have to ask Patti for a few pointers.

"You're smiling," he said. "Anything I should know about?"

She shook her head. "There's coffee, if you want some."

Alex poured them each a mug. Larkin worked in silence. She wanted to turn on the radio but felt the gesture might seem rude. Was it possible that she had spent the most intense hours of her life in the arms of this man? At the moment, simple conversation seemed beyond their ability. Even the ordinary act of carrying a plate of food to the table took extraordinary effort.

"You're a good cook," Alex said. "This is terrific."

"Breakfasts are my specialty. I used to help my mother when I was growing up."

"That's right. You were the only daughter, weren't you?"

She poured milk into her coffee. "That I was. I never left the kitchen until I was thirteen." Why on earth had she said something so stupid? She made it sound as though she'd been used as the Walker family charwoman, which was far from accurate. "What I mean to say is, my mother believed a daughter should know her way around the kitchen."

"The way to a man's heart?"

"Precisely, although I never fully believed a pot roast was the key to happily ever after."

Alex's laugh was forced, unnatural. "Lasagna, maybe," he said. "Not pot roast."

Another silence.

"I get *The New York Times* delivered," she said. "If you'd like to read it or tackle the crossword puzzle, I—"

He shook his head. "Thanks, anyway. I don't think clearly until noon on the weekends."

She was desperately searching for another topic of conversation when the phone rang and she leaped up to answer it. She didn't have to be an aging prizefighter to understand the meaning of the words "saved by the bell."

IF ALEX THOUGHT he felt stupid wearing his pirate getup at the gas station the night before, that was only a warm-up for the way he felt sitting at Larkin's breakfast table that morning. Everything between them last night had been blessed by a touch of magic; their elaborate costumes only enhanced the illusion.

Today, however, he felt like a first-class fool sitting there at her kitchen table like a barefoot Sinbad the Sailor. The only way it could have been worse would be if he still had his earring on.

When the phone rang and she jumped up to answer it—despite the fact that she usually relied upon her machine—he abandoned all pretense of eating and listened to her chat and laugh with Roger Lacey about the party last night.

Alex had almost forgotten that there had ever been a Halloween party at Roger's house. All he could remember was the reality of Larkin in his arms, the heady scent of her perfume, the sound of her voice murmuring his name in his ear.

When he had awakened that morning and heard her bustling around the kitchen, he'd been filled with elation—an elation he'd last known when Rikki was alive. He knew Larkin wasn't Rikki—he didn't want her to be—but the sense of joy he felt thinking about her was the same joy he'd felt during his marriage.

He'd been on his way into the kitchen to lure Larkin into the shower with him when he spotted a copy of *People* and an issue of the *Star* on top of her dressing table. Vladimir Karpov's splendid face looked up at him from both covers, and Alex had to exercise the utmost control to keep from flushing them down the john.

Jealousy had been an unknown emotion to him before meeting Larkin, and he wasn't proud of the things he wondered about, the questions he'd like to ask her about Karpov. So Alex showered alone and tried to rein in his conflicting emotions for the time being.

Apparently, he wasn't doing a very good job of it, because at the moment he even resented Roger Lacey's place in her life.

"Sorry I took so long," Larkin said as she came back into the kitchen and sat down. "Roger loves to do a postmortem on all his parties. I had to cut him short halfway through his guest list."

"Did he have anything to say about me?" The question came out before he could stop it.

She gave him a funny half-smile. "He liked your earring, and your boots were to die for."

He refilled his coffee cup and topped off Larkin's. "He should be glad he doesn't have to wear them in broad daylight."

Once again the conversation fell dead. They ate in silence until his beeper sounded.

"Busy morning," he said. "May I use the phone?"

"Use the one in the bedroom," she said. "More privacy."

Five minutes later he was standing at her front door, in full pirate regalia, saying goodbye to the woman he was falling in love with as if she were no more than a casual acquaintance.

"I'm sorry to be leaving so abruptly," he said, fishing his car keys out of the pocket of his tight black pants. "I never expected an emergency to pop up today."

"Don't apologize. Emergencies rarely pop up on schedule. I understand."

She more than understood. Alex had seen the look of relief on her face when he told her he was needed by a patient. She seemed as eager for him to leave as he was.

"My weekends usually aren't work-oriented," he said.

"Mine are," she said.

Morning sun reflected in her eyes as they stood in the doorway, and he was hard put to interpret what he saw there. He stepped outside to the top stair.

"Drive carefully."

He grinned. "The patient's in Rhode Island."

"You're flying today?"

"Want to come?" Hell, why not take one last stab at breaking through the barriers between them.

"Sorry. I have some work to catch up on at the school."

He reached out and touched her cheek. "Thank you, Larkin." Her beautiful green eyes looked away, but his intensity drew them back to his. "Last night was more than I—"

She placed her finger on his mouth. "I know," she said. "For me, as well."

He wanted to tell·her that he, the psychologist, understood what was going on, that what had happened between them had been so volatile, so potentially shattering to their future—both separately and together—that they needed time to step back and reevaluate.

Unfortunately, the psychologist wasn't in love with Larkin Walker; the man was, and at the moment, the man was at a loss for words.

LARKIN HATED the Learning Center on Saturdays.

All the Saturday classes were held in parks and museums and other points of interest, and the school itself seemed about as lively as a ghost town. Today, however, the isolation suited her just fine. She had a lot of paperwork to contend with surrounding Vladimir's upcoming workshop, and even her dreary, deserted office was preferable·to sitting at home alone with her confusion.

Where had the magic between her and Alex disappeared? It had been there when she fell asleep, cradled in his arms; yet, by the time she awoke it was gone. He had seemed to blot out everything with the sheer power of his masculinity, and the ease with which she had surrendered unnerved her.

Retreat seemed the wisest course.

So she sat at her desk through the long afternoon, trying to come up with a glamorous way to publicize a glamorous star. Vladimir expected a great deal of free publicity in return for speaking at the Center, and Larkin was hard put to come up with something glitzy enough, yet still within her operating budget. She came up with ideas for invitation-only dinners and black-tie receptions only to reject each idea out of hand.

At the moment she really didn't give a damn if the whole event ever came off at all.

Despite the large breakfast she'd eaten a few hours earlier, Larkin was hungry again around noon, and she killed two hours by searching around for a deli with the perfect tuna-salad sandwich. She had a yen for an almond bar—more emotional than biological, this time—but she decided to exercise her willpower and refuse to give in. If she kept eating like this, her relationship with Alex Jakobs would put ten pounds on her before she knew what hit her.

Finally, at around four o'clock, she decided that Vladimir would simply have to accept newspaper publicity and a direct-mail blitz and let word of mouth take care of the rest. If his ego needed more stroking than that, let his publicist deal with it. She was too tired, too cranky and too cold to care.

There was no longer any point in pretending that Alex wasn't uppermost in her mind. Her attempt at sidestepping the issue had failed miserably, and now she was going to go home to try to make some sense out of the way she was feeling. When she was younger, she had tumbled headfirst into love, unaware of the danger. Now she was older and wiser—still prone to tumbling headfirst, but not without a fight.

THE EARTH DROPPED AWAY from the Cessna and he was airborne. The small plane rocked in the light head wind, then gained altitude steadily, and Alex settled in for the short hop to Providence. He loved the brief uncertainty of takeoff, when it seemed as if gravity would win the battle and keep him chained to the earth.

Rikki used to say that he was the only man alive who enjoyed turbulence, and he always laughed but never denied it. His entire life had been predicated on the fact that the impossible could be attained, and keeping a plane aloft despite tricky air currents and the threat of wind shear fit right in with that philosophy.

Today, however, the turbulence was all inside him, and when he landed in Providence and discovered that the emergency had already been taken care of, his body vibrated with an excess of emotion and energy.

He paced up and down the length of the observation deck of the small private airport. Hadn't they decided they needed some time and space to reestablish their boundaries? Hadn't he wanted to get as far away as possible from Larkin Walker before he found himself hopelessly entangled in her life?

He stopped in his tracks. Hadn't he also promised never to lie to himself?

Any new boundaries they established would be established within their new relationship. And as for getting away before he became entangled in Larkin's life, it was already too late for that. When she first came into his arms, any hope of keeping his heart intact went up in smoke, and whether he liked it or not, Alex Jakobs fell in love.

THE DATSUN'S ENGINE wheezed and rattled and stubbornly refused to turn over no matter how many times Larkin tried. She let out the clutch and fought down the urge to get out and kick the damned car in its rear quarter-panel.

Her mechanic's fourteenth warning about the alarming age of her battery rang in her ears, and the cost of another tow-truck call conjured up visions of many nights of peanut-butter-and jelly dinners.

No wonder her mother liked being married. There was always somebody around to take care of annoying incidentals like batteries and brake jobs.

Larkin was on her way back inside the Center to call her service station when she heard the familiar roar of Gordon Franklin's ancient car.

"You have no idea how happy I am to see you!" she said as he pulled up next to her car. "You're the answer to my prayers."

For once Gordon didn't turn red with embarrassment. "I was driving by and I saw your car. Is something wrong?"

Larkin laughed. "Wrong? Only everything." She gestured toward the red Datsun with disgust. "I'm dying to go home and take a long, hot bath, and the car decides to die on me."

"Release the hood lock."

Larkin reached inside the car and pulled the handle. The hood popped and Gordon raised it into position.

"You didn't get the new battery Monty told you to get." He looked very stern and very young, and she had to bite back a smile.

"Guilty. I just haven't had time to drop the car off." His frown deepened. "Don't look like that, Gordon. I thought I could get another few months out of it."

"You're lucky you weren't alone on the Expressway at night. What would you have done then?"

"Prayed for a police car to drive by. I promise I'll have the battery replaced on Monday." He was fiddling with the battery terminals, and she leaned over his shoulder to see exactly what he was doing. "Can you fix it, Gordon?"

He inserted one of his house keys into the battery connection. "Try it now."

She got into the car, put it into neutral, and turned the key.

"You're a miracle worker! Gordon, how can I ever thank you enough?"

He removed his key from the terminal and closed the hood. "By getting a new battery," he said. "I may not always be here when you need me."

"Of course you will be, Gordon," she said. "You've never let me down."

His customary blush blossomed, and impulsively she kissed him on the cheek. He looked at her, and in that look she saw wonderment and longing and a sadness that brought tears to her eyes. However, before she could put a name to it, it was gone and his expression was once more guarded.

"Go right home," he said. "Don't turn the engine off or you won't be able to get it started again."

"It's a promise," she said as she got back into her car. "Thanks again, Gordon. I really appreciate your help."

He flashed a quick, shy smile in her general direction and climbed behind the wheel of his Chevy. "Drive carefully," he said, and before she could get her car into gear, he roared out of the parking lot and back into traffic.

Whatever Gordon did to the car worked, because Larkin was able to drive the fifteen miles to her house with no problem. How he had managed to resurrect her car from the dead with a house key was a mystery to her. She wished he were more comfortable in her presence, because she would have liked to take him to lunch or something to thank him for all the many favors, both large and small, that he performed for her that were not in the course of duty.

She turned down her block, squinting against the late-afternoon glare. Maybe if she invited Patti to come along he wouldn't feel quite—

Her fatigue was worse than she thought. For a second she imagined she saw a shiny dark gray Buick parked in front of one of her neighbor's houses.

"It's a good night's sleep for you tonight, Walker," she muttered as she pulled into the driveway.

She turned off the engine and got out, and as she reached for her pocketbook in the back seat, she saw Alex sitting on the top step by her front door with a basket of violets by his side.

She walked toward him, acutely aware of every movement she made. He never took his eyes from her.

"Violets—in November?" She buried her nose in the mass of violets. "You must be a magician."

"I'm no magician," Alex said. "There's a wonderful nursery in Newport that caters to intrepid romantics."

"I thought you had an emergency in Providence," she said, unlocking her front door.

Alex stood on the bottom step. "Things were settled by the time I got there. I used the time to do some thinking."

"Come to any conclusions?"

He smiled at her, and she thought her heart would burst through her chest. "Only that I want to be near you tonight."

"Funny thing," she said, opening the door, "I did some thinking today myself."

A flicker of apprehension passed across his handsome face. "Come to any conclusions?"

"Just one."

"Which is?"

She smiled at him. "Come in and I'll show you."

Chapter Twelve

"I don't believe it," Larkin mumbled, burrowing her face more closely against Alex's chest. "Who would call at this ungodly hour?"

Alex squinted at the digital clock on the end table. "It's not that ungodly an hour," he said, noting the sunshine trying to get through the cracks in the venetian blinds. "It's eight-fourteen."

The phone shrilled again.

"Eight-fourteen on a Sunday morning *is* ungodly," she said with a groan. "No decent person is even awake yet."

He decided not to go into the fact that they had only drifted into sleep an hour ago after a night of the most incredible physical and emotional communion he'd ever known. The answering machine clicked on and they both waited.

Beep. "Larkin, I know you're in there. Wake up! Larkin?"

"Is that Patti?"

Larkin sat up. "I'm going to kill her! If she wants to tell me about one of her dates, I'll—"

Patti's voice was more insistent this time. "Larkin! I'm not joking. This is an emergency. The balloon trip has—"

Larkin leaned over Alex and picked up the telephone. "Has there been an accident?"

Patti was speaking so loudly that he had no difficulty in hearing her side of the conversation.

"Accident? How can there be an accident if we haven't even gotten off the ground yet?"

"Slow down, Patti!" She was still leaning over him and her breasts brushed against his thighs. He hoped it would be a long phone call. "Start at the beginning. What the hell is going on?"

Patti sounded as if she were on the verge of hysteria. A planned hot-air balloon excursion in southern New Jersey fizzled when the pilot failed to show up. The charter bus wouldn't return for them until three o'clock, and Patti was stranded in a meadow with a group of irate patrons who were looking to have Larkin's head.

"You have to get here fast. One of them is from *The New York Times*. He'll kill the Center if we don't come up with something."

Fascinated, Alex watched as Larkin's mind jumped into overdrive.

"Are you still in O'Hanlon's pasture?"

"Yes, but—"

"Stay there, she ordered. "Break out the champagne breakfast you brought for after the flight. I'll be there as soon as I can."

"But it's a two-hour drive!"

She looked at Alex in question and he nodded.

"I'll be there before you know it, Patti. Trust me."

She hung up the phone, then lingered a moment on his lap. "I really appreciate this, Alex."

"Are you sure you want to fly with me?"

"I have no choice, have I? I have to get to New Jersey as fast as I can."

"Thanks for the vote of confidence," he said dryly. "Are you sure you don't want to take out flight insurance?"

She grinned. "Do you offer it?"

He ran his fingers through her long hair and let it trail over his belly and thighs. "I've never needed it."

Her eyes widened. "You fly without insurance?"

"It's known as living dangerously."

She turned a shade paler. "That isn't what I wanted to hear, Alex."

"You've flown before. What are you so afraid of?"

"Death. Dismemberment, pain... You name it, I'm afraid of it."

"And you offer a 'Fear of Flying' seminar?" He shook his head. "You take care of your students. I'll take care of transportation."

"I'm putting my life in your hands."

"Trust me." He gave her a friendly swat on the derriere.

She looked at him as if he were a hand grenade ready to explode, and he laughed. "Get ready to go. All I have to do is call the airport and file a flight plan and we're on our way."

"I'M NOT GOING UP in that station wagon with wings," Larkin said thirty minutes later as she inspected Alex's Cessna 207. "You must think I'm crazy."

"It's safer than driving on the Expressway."

"So's skydiving, but I'm not signing up for a jump."

He chuckled and continued his preflight routine. Morning sun picked up the blond highlights in his chestnut hair and gave him a younger, more carefree look. Before today, she had seen Alex dressed only in three-piece suits and his pirate costume, and she was intrigued by how at ease he seemed in jeans, shirt and a battered leather jacket.

The faded jeans fit snugly around his lean hips and legs, and the black jacket emphasized the width of his shoulders. All signs of Alex Jakobs., Ph.D., were gone. The man in front of her was obviously born to fly.

He opened the passenger door and she climbed inside. It was going to take more than the frayed seat belt to keep her inside this thing. He closed the door behind her.

"I've changed my mind," she said as Alex got into the pilot's seat and slipped on his headset. "This really isn't such a good idea."

He started the engine. The one puny propeller on the nose of the plane began to spin. "Do you have any other ideas on how to get to Patti?"

"I can drive," she yelled over the engine noise.

"It will take you over two hours, Larkin."

He fiddled with some gauges and dials and mumbled something into his mouthpiece. The plane began to shudder.

"I'll take a train," she said as the plane eased over to the end of the line of equally tiny planes awaiting clearance for takeoff.

"By the time you figure out the train schedules, the bus will have taken them all back home." His grin was wicked and wise. "Face it, Larkin: we're going for a ride."

She closed her eyes and prepared to die. When it was their turn to take off, Alex wound the motor up and they barreled down the short runway, then, miraculously, took to the air.

"It couldn't wait to leave the ground," Larkin said as she opened her eyes. "You weren't going more than sixty miles an hour when we took off."

"Perfect economy of design," Alex said, as the Cessna gained altitude, leaving the airport and the surrounding suburbs behind. "She's doing what she was made to do."

And so, it seemed, was he.

"I appreciate this more than I can say, Alex. I'm sure this wasn't how you'd planned to spend your Sunday morning."

The plane banked left. "No, it wasn't. I'd planned to spend it in bed with you, but since we seem to have a definite problem with mornings, this was the next-best thing."

Normally, Larkin would have argued that being trapped in a plane was second best only to death by torture. She was accustomed to the tin-can atmosphere on commercial jet planes: the strange-smelling recycled air combined with the cramped seats and pressurized cabin gave her claustrophobia before the plane even left the runway.

This, however, was different. She could literally reach outside the window and touch the clouds. The mystery of flight was less terrifying when she could actually see the dials and gauges and instruments responsible for keeping the plane aloft. And, of course, there was Alex. Watching him as he kept the plane on course, listening to him as he explained exactly what was going on, knowing that she was sharing an important part of his life, she found it possible to forget that in a little while she would be coping with twenty irate customers and a near-hysterical Patti Franklin.

As difficult as the morning before had been, that's how easy this morning was. On both nights the physical aspects of lovemaking had been exciting beyond Larkin's wildest fantasies. Last night, however, something else had been added, a secret, magical element that transcended sex and raised their pleasure to a higher level. Some might label the magic "love." Larkin wasn't ready to go quite that far, but if love meant feeling you could soar out into the tranquil blue skies over Long Island without benefit of a one-engine Cessna 207—well, maybe she'd have to consider the possibility.

"IS SHE ALWAYS LIKE THIS?" Alex turned to Patti, who was leaning against the side of the car Larkin had managed to rent at the Princeton airport.

"This is nothing," Patti said, reapplying her crimson lipstick. "I saw her convince a tongue-tied archaeologist that he'd like nothing better than to conduct a two-day dig off Montauk Point."

"The only thing off Montauk Point is the Atlantic Ocean, Patti."

She grinned at him. "See what I mean? The woman is amazing."

That she was.

From the second they reached the farm where Patti was stranded with the would-be balloonists, Larkin had been a whirlwind of energy and invention.

He had expected unfocused anger, abject apologies and random confusion. Instead, he watched, amazed, as she charmed and flirted and practically bribed her way past their well-founded fury and began to turn adversity into adventure. It was a brazen mixture of humility and humbug, and it worked beautifully. He was duly impressed.

Alex was even more impressed a half hour later when he found himself called into service for the cause. O'Hanlon, the farmer on whose property they were stranded, agreed to open his house to the refugees from the Learning Center, and Larkin was going to teach an impromptu dance class for those who were interested. Patti would offer a lesson from the "How to Flirt" course she gave four times a year.

Alex suddenly found himself volunteering to take passengers up in his Cessna for an impromptu aerial tour of Princeton University and the environs thereof. Later on, when he had time to think about it, he wasn't sure if the idea had originated with him or the wily Ms Walker. However, one thing he was sure of was that he was having the time of his life.

At around two o'clock he refueled his plane for the third time and was about to fly back to O'Hanlon's when he saw Larkin sitting on the hood of the rented car.

"Bring on the horde," he called as he walked toward her. "I'm back in service again."

She stood up. Her hair glowed with platinum highlights in the fierce sunlight, and it flowed freely over her shoulders and to her waist. "I know this will break your heart," she said with a grin, "but you're off the hook."

"I'm off the hook?"

"No more barnstorming the skies over Princeton. The bus came early and the horde is on its way back home."

"I thought we'd get in at least one more flight."

"No," she said. "Your prayers were answered. I—" His face must have given him away, because Larkin suddenly stopped. "You're not disappointed, are you?"

He shrugged. "What can I say? I was having a great time."

She came over to where he stood and put her arms around his waist.

"Have you ever considered giving up psychology and taking to the skies?"

"Every now and then," he admitted. "Especially now that *Helpline* will be on twice a week."

"Live both nights?"

"Afraid so."

She sighed. "We should have Patti feed our schedules into the computer to see if we're compatible."

"We're compatible," he said. "I think we proved that last night."

"It's not the nights I worry about. It's the mornings that seem to give us trouble." She kissed his jaw. "Next time I promise to disconnect the phone."

The words "next time" echoed inside him. "I'll turn off the beeper."

"If you could arrange to wear that pirate costume again, I wouldn't complain."

She managed to look both angelic and wickedly sexy, and he laughed. "Sounds a little kinky, Ms Walker. Care to talk about it?"

"Personally or professionally?"

He pulled her close. "Personally."

"I'd much rather show you what I mean when we get home, Dr. Jakobs."

He feigned surprise. "You'll actually risk flying with me again?"

"Well, I had been considering Amtrak—"

"Life is a series of risks, Larkin. Live dangerously." Absurd advice from a man who had been avoiding emotional risk-taking for the past four years.

"I have," she said.

He couldn't read the expression on her face. She suddenly seemed distant, and he wondered if she was thinking about Vladimir Karpov, wishing for what once was. Challenging tricky air currents in his Cessna was about the biggest risk he'd ever taken before meeting Larkin.

Vladimir Karpov, however, would be back in town in just three weeks.

The thought of a midair collision didn't scare Alex half as much.

JAYNE WALKER'S INTUITION was still in fine working order. That night, after Larkin and Alex had said a reluctant good-night to each other, Jayne called long-distance.

"Your phone's been busy all evening, honey," Jayne said. "Are you working on Sundays now, too?"

True to her promise, Larkin had taken the phone off the hook as soon as she and Alex returned to her house. That fact, however, was not one to share with a parent.

"Seven days a week, Mom," she said truthfully. She told her mother about that morning's balloon fiasco that had been miraculously turned around. "Even the reporter from *The New York Times* seemed happy when he left."

"Is this the same Alex Jakobs you went to Roger's party with?" Leave it to Jayne to cut right through to the essentials.

"Yes, it is."

"Are you seeing a lot of him?"

"Some."

"You're being evasive, Larkin."

"You're being nosy, Mom."

"That's a mother's prerogative."

"Sometimes I think you forget I'm thirty years old. Do you pester Jordan and Billy and Ed and Barry this way?"

"They're all married. I don't have to pester them."

"If I get married, will you stop pestering me?"

"Well, I won't make any promises, but . . ."

"That's almost enough to make me consider walking down the aisle."

"Is Alex a candidate?"

"We haven't known each other that long, Mom."

"Your father and I knew each other only two weeks when we married."

"Maybe I'm not as daring as you are."

"Are you sure that's the only reason?"

Larkin recognized that tone in her mother's voice only too well. "What do you mean, Mother?"

"He's a widower, Larkin. It takes some men a long time to let go."

"He's a psychologist. He seems to have a healthy attitude about it." She hesitated. "I think I'm the one with the problem." She told Jayne about how often she thought of Rikki Jakobs. "So many times I have to stop myself from asking a million questions about her." Questions Jayne would rather not hear.

"It's normal to be jealous, honey."

Larkin shuddered. "But Rikki's dead, Mom. How can I be jealous of someone who is no longer a threat?"

"You're jealous of all she's shared with him. She obviously helped shape the man he's become, and that scares you."

"Are you sure you don't have a degree in psychology hiding somewhere?" Jayne's insight into Larkin was often painfully on target.

"Just common sense. Does your Alex know about Vladimir Karpov?"

Larkin's face reddened. "Obliquely. Of course he knows Vladimir will be speaking at the Center."

"How does Alex feel about that?"

"How should he feel? It's a business arrangement, Mother."

"You don't believe that any more than I do, Larkin."

"I'm sorry to disappoint you, but I do believe it."

"I doubt if Alex Jakobs thinks of it as only a business arrangement."

Larkin's temper sizzled. "What does Alex have to do with this? He isn't a silent partner in the Center."

"When a woman's first love comes back on the scene, I wouldn't blame a man for not liking it."

"I don't care if Alex likes or dislikes it. Vladimir is going to be in town and I'm happy about it. Business should go through the roof."

"There's more than business to think about here, Larkin. How about Alex's feelings?"

"I wish for once you would stop worrying about men and their damned egos and hang-ups!" The Walker household had always revolved around her father and her brothers. "Maybe if you'd been more concerned with your own rights, you'd still have your own career."

"I didn't want my career any longer, Larkin. I wanted a family."

"And now that your family is grown?"

Jayne didn't miss a beat. "I have my grandchildren and your father. I'm a happy woman, Larkin, whether or not you approve of my decisions."

Of course, Larkin knew that. She couldn't have lived eighteen years in her parents' house and not have been aware of the real love that existed between Jayne and Bill Walker. But Jayne's way and Larkin's were not the same. With Vladimir, Larkin had turned over her life to him and existed only as an extension. Vladimir had neither Bill Walker's devotion nor his integrity, and her pain had taught Larkin a bitter lesson.

No matter how much she cared for Alex, she would never make that mistake again—not even to be like his beloved Rikki.

"Do you get the feeling we've covered this territory before?" Larkin asked finally.

"Once or twice," Jayne said. "I didn't mean to pry, honey. It's just that I love you and I want you to be happy."

Larkin's eyes filled with quick, hot tears. "I know," she managed. "I don't mean to be so critical of your choices, Mom. Things just aren't that clear-cut for me."

"I wish they were."

Larkin smiled. "So do I."

"Just because times have changed, don't think everything has, honey. People still want the same things they've always wanted. Love and families never go out of style."

They said goodbye and Larkin hung up the phone. Her mother had brought some very painful issues out into the open, and Larkin wasn't entirely sure she was ready to think about any of them. What was wrong with simply enjoying what she and Alex had at the moment and being satisfied with that?

Jayne believed in happy endings. Larkin had learned that life rarely provided them. Weren't Rikki's death and Vladimir's infidelity proof of that? Even Jayne's intrepid optimism couldn't guarantee that Larkin and Alex's romance would withstand the rigors of reality.

It was no wonder that brownies were so popular. There was nothing like chocolate to soothe a tortured soul.

Larkin got up and headed toward the kitchen.

THE BEARDED MAN acted as if he owned her. He pulled her into his arms at the front door and the way the man looked at her, as if she were a possession, made him burn with rage.

At first he wanted to leap from the shadows and spring for his throat, but he'd managed to battle down that primitive instinct. No, there were better ways, more permanent ways to deal with this.

So he followed him north, keeping a safe distance along the dark and winding roads, just managing to keep the lights of the gray Buick in his vision.

Now he watched as the man let himself into the big house on the hill. Lights appeared in the window, and the man's large silhouette was visible as he crossed the room to hang up his coat.

His name was on the mailbox at the end of the driveway in letters large enough for a half-blind man to read. The more he knew about this man, the easier it would be to protect her.

But first he needed to remind the man that things weren't always as they seemed.

IT SOUNDED LIKE a brick hitting the front door. Alex was in the master bathroom shaving, and he jumped as the crash echoed through the quiet house.

"Damn it to hell!" Blood trickled down his neck and he swiped at it with a towel. *Damn kids extending Halloween an extra few days.* He wrapped a towel around his middle and ran barefoot down the hallway to the front door and flung it open.

Two mourning doves lay on the top step. They had been strangled with a length of gold chain. Their bodies rested at right angles to each other in a grotesque parody of sleep.

There was no sign of anyone around. Whoever was responsible for this disgusting prank had disappeared. He untangled the chain from around the poor creatures' necks and held it in his hand. Casual violence disgusted him and made him despair for the human condition. He knew it had been Halloween weekend; he knew people would say, "Kids will be kids." But he also knew a hell of a lot about human nature, and his instincts told him that no kid out for a perverted lark would leave behind a chain as expensive as this one.

He went back into the house and put the chain in the top drawer of his desk. Call it paranoia, but he wanted to hang on to it. Something about this whole thing didn't sit right with him. The craftsmanship of the chain, the precise angle at which the birds had been placed—it all seemed too deliberate, too symbolic, to be easily shrugged off as a simple prank.

The birds were a message, but the meaning of the message eluded him, leaving just an underlying sense of foreboding that he couldn't shake.

He dressed and went outside to bury the birds in a shallow grave in his backyard.

Chapter Thirteen

Tuesday morning's class, "Good Dog–Bad Dog, or Thirty Days to a Perfect Puppy," did not turn out to be one of Larkin's better ideas.

"Remind me to strike this from next semester's catalog," she said to Patti as she lugged her bucket of cleanser and hot water into the classroom. "Perfect parakeets, maybe, but I'm convinced there's no such thing as a perfect puppy."

Patti was busy vacuuming dog hairs from the furniture and drapes. "Not even that cute little schnauzer with the overbite?"

"Especially the schnauzer." She pointed to the southwest corner of the room. "That's his calling card over there."

Patti unplugged the vacuum cleaner. "The owners seemed to have a terrific time."

Larkin pulled the sponge from the hot soapy water and began scrubbing the floor. "The owners don't have to clean up. Of course they had a terrific time."

"Five of them asked Art if he'd do a follow-up course."

"On what? How to destroy a classroom?"

"The puppies would be older," Patti reasoned. "They'll probably be housebroken by then."

Larkin sat back on her heels and rinsed the sponge in a bucket of clear water. "They'll also be bigger. I don't think I could face this again. With my luck, we'd have a class of Great Danes."

Patti laughed, and Larkin threatened to throw the wet sponge at her—a dire threat, but effective. Patti grabbed an extra one, and they were scrubbing and gossiping when Gordon popped up at the door.

"Grab a sponge," Larkin said, brushing her hair out of her face with the side of her arm. "The more the merrier."

Gordon immediately began rolling up his sleeves.

"I'm only kidding," Larkin said, shaking her head. "We're almost done."

Patti glared at her younger brother. "Where were you when we really needed you?"

"Working on the paneling upstairs." He reddened as he turned to Larkin. "You should have paged me, Larkin. I would've come right down."

Gordon's hands were actually shaking and Larkin's heart went out to him. "We'll leave the buckets for you to empty," she said, shooting Patti a fierce look. "Your sister's in a rotten mood because a Pomeranian relieved himself on her suede boots. Pay no attention to her."

Gordon met Larkin's eyes for a second, and she was surprised once again at how beautiful a shade of blue his were. Then he mumbled something about going to the hardware store for some finishing nails and disappeared down the hall.

"Gordon's not made of porcelain," Patti said as soon as her brother was out of earshot. "He can stand a little sisterly teasing, Larkin."

Larkin scrubbed at a particularly stubborn stain on the tile floor. "When he blushes like that, my maternal instincts are aroused," she said. "He's been doing so well lately. I'd hate to see him crawl back into his shell."

"Losing our parents was hard on him," Patti said. "I've always been the tough one. It's hard for me to understand you more sensitive souls."

"Why don't we have dinner tonight?" she asked Patti impulsively. "We could go down to Captain Bill's. I haven't had fisherman's chowder in ages."

"Don't get me wrong. I'd love to go to Captain Bill's with you, but this is ladies' night at Private Eyes."

"You're incorrigible. Can't Private Eyes do without you one night?"

"I have my reputation to consider, but I suppose I still have to eat."

"Reservations for six o'clock?"

"Sounds great. Do you suppose I could convince you to join me at the club later?"

Larkin wrinkled her nose. "Somehow I doubt I'd fit in, Patti." She gestured toward her flowing hair and soft peach cashmere dress. Private Eyes was a new-wave club where women looked like Madonna or Cyndi Lauper, not like an ex-ballerina.

"Don't worry," Patti said. "We could punk your hair and add a camouflage jacket."

Larkin grinned. "I'll take it under advisement." She brushed some dust off her skirt and stood up. "Come on. I want to run through the mailing list on the ballet series."

"We got the photos from Karpov's publicist this morning." Patti feigned a swoon. "My dear, I am counting the days until the twenty-ninth."

"And here I thought you would schedule your vacation that week."

"Listen, I'd pay *you* that week if I had to."

Larkin led the way down the hall to her office. "Don't give me any ideas, Patti. I just might take you up on that offer. We need Vladimir's lecture series to help balance our budget."

The Learning Center was a word-of-mouth success, but that success had not yet translated into financial security. Larkin was banking on Vladimir Karpov's lecture series to get them some major-league publicity that would put the school on the map.

Larkin sat down at her desk and looked at the publicity photos of Vladimir. Patti lit a cigarette and leaned over her shoulder, whistling appreciatively at each new eight-by-ten glossy.

"No one really looks like that," Patti said. "Tell me he's the product of airbrushing and backlighting."

Larkin looked at one still of Vladimir leaping across the stage, all of his power and beauty trapped in flight, and shook her head. "I wish I could," she said. "Unfortunately, what you see is what there is."

"Is there any regulation about employees mingling socially with speakers?" Patti sat down on the couch by Larkin's desk.

Some unexpected memories rose to the surface, and Larkin turned the photos face-down on her desk. "Should I come up with one?"

"I just want to know the rules," Patti said. "I value your friendship, and if you'd rather I not make a play for the Russian Wonder, I'll—"

"You're a big girl, Patti. I wouldn't dream of telling you what to do." A twinge of unfocused jealousy pinched, and she dismissed it. "I just hope you remember what I've told you about Vladimir. He plays by his own rules, and those rules usually work against the woman in his arms."

"I think it's worth the risk," Patti said, picking up one of the shirtless-torso shots and smiling broadly. "Think of the memories I'll have to warm me in my old age."

Larkin said nothing. Memories, she had found, were scant warmth on a cold winter's night. Unfortunately, that was something Patti would have to find out for herself.

ALEX WHIPPED HIS car into the empty spot next to Larkin's and grinned when he noticed the aviator's glasses he'd given her dangling from her sun visor. He was en route from his class at Dowling College on the South Shore to his taping at the studio on the North Shore, and he'd decided to stop to see if Larkin was free for lunch.

A call from Judy that morning had reminded him that Cameron's birthday was this Friday. Judy asked him if he'd like to invite Larkin.

"Very romantic idea, Judy," he'd said through his laughter. "I'm sure she'd get a real kick out of mingling with the *Sesame Street* set."

"I'm not going to chain you to the house, Alex," Judy said, highly affronted. "Maybe it would be good for the two of you to get away for a day or two. You have said your schedules are crazy."

The idea began to have its charm. "And maybe you and Phil want to meet Larkin?"

Judy's laugh had clinched the deal.

Phil and Judy were the closest thing to a family that he had on earth. Introducing them to Larkin, sharing this part of his past with her, was a logical next step in their relationship.

He grinned, thinking of the way he felt when he was near her. Logic rarely played a part in his emotions with Larkin. He headed across the parking lot at a run. For the first time in years, he felt eager, filled with a cautious optimism that gave each day a luster that had been missing from his life for quite a while.

He was whistling when he burst in the front door of the Center and ran headlong into Gordon Franklin.

"I'm sorry," he said, grabbing the young man's arms to keep him from tumbling to the carpeted floor of the reception room. "I wasn't watching. Are you hurt?"

Gordon shook his head. His dark hair flopped over his forehead, dipping below his brows. He kept his eyes averted.

"They should put a stoplight here," Alex said, trying to draw the young man into conversation. "They must average six crack-ups a week." He watched as Gordon flexed one arm. "Are you sure I didn't hurt you?"

"You didn't hurt me." Gordon looked up and Alex instinctively stepped back. Hate—pure and unmistakable—burned in Gordon's blue eyes. Then, before Alex could say anything, Gordon smiled slightly, and the look disappeared. "I'm on my way to the hardware store. I wasn't watching where I was going."

Alex watched as the young man loped across the blacktop parking lot and climbed behind the wheel of his ancient car.

I must be going crazy, he thought. Had he simply imagined that look of pure venom in Gordon's eyes? It had passed over the young man's face so swiftly that now, just moments later, Alex couldn't remember exactly what it was he had seen in Gordon's eyes.

Alex had no doubt that Gordon was crazy about Larkin—and he could certainly understand all the reasons why. However, infatuation and obsession were two entirely different things, and just because Alex was feeling a bit threatened these days as Karpov's workshops approached, there was no reason to paint darker motives on a young man's fantasy.

Serious thoughts, these. Yet they all went flying out of Alex's head as soon as he walked into Larkin's office. She was bent over a stack of photographs. Her long amber hair waved across one shoulder and she nibbled thoughtfully on the eraser end of a pencil. He would have been happy to spend the rest of his life simply watching her breathe.

"You realize the entire population of Liechtenstein could have walked into this school unnoticed, don't you?"

She looked up, her eyes widening first in surprise, then in pleasure. "Our security force is very discreet," she said, rising to greet him. "They instantly recognized you as the illustrious Alex Jakobs, Ph.D., and granted you safe passage."

He kissed her. "Difficult morning?"

"You must be psychic."

"Not psychic." They sat down together on her sofa. "I tasted chocolate."

"The puppy obedience class sent me running for the almond bars." She crossed her legs, and he had a tantalizing glimpse of slender thigh. "What brings you here on a Tuesday morning?"

He glanced at his watch. It was just noon. "Tuesday afternoon," he corrected. "Can you be convinced to slip out for lunch with me?"

She glanced toward the stack of photos on her desk. "I'd love to, but—"

"No apologies," he said easily. "This was short notice. I just wanted an excuse to see you in the middle of the day."

"Don't you have to get to the studio for your taping?"

"I have until three o'clock."

"Any other Tuesday afternoon would be fine," she said, obviously dismayed, "but I'm expecting a phone call at one, and I have a stack of promo material to go through for the ballet series. We go to press tonight on the brochures."

A tiny flame of jealousy flickered to life. "Karpov?" It took all of his self-control not to lean over to look at the photos on her desk.

Larkin nodded. The high color in her cheeks gave away her discomfort. "We're only three weeks away from the first lecture."

They were quiet for a few moments. Then Larkin said, "Why don't we call out for something? Just because I can't leave doesn't mean we can't have lunch."

He plunged his hand into her hair and let it slip, silky and fragrant, through his fingers. "I'm really not that hungry."

"Neither am I."

"Is anybody around?"

"Patti's in the computer room, and Sharon should be back at the reception desk."

"Would a closed door elicit any talk?"

"Probably." Larkin stood up. "But talk has never bothered me before." She closed the door to her office and locked it.

She came into his arms. Her dress was soft as angel's hair beneath his hands and the scent of Bal à Versailles evoked memories of their lovemaking. Thoughts of inviting her to Virginia drifted out of his mind. Over her shoulder he saw a photo of Karpov separate from the rest. He was leaning against a wall, bronzed and blond and magnificent, arms folded across his chest, an enigmatic smile on his narrow face. The fact that the woman in his arms now had once loved that blond giant aroused feelings in Alex that could best be described as barbaric.

But then she raised her face to him, her green eyes smoky and dark, her lips slightly parted.

"Now, what was it you came here to convince me to do?" she asked lazily. "Lunch, was it?"

He swept her into his arms. "To hell with lunch," he said and carried her over to the sofa. He needed to drive Karpov's image from Larkin's mind—and from his own, as well.

NO LONGER WAS HE ALEX the gentle lover of the past few nights. This man in her office made love to her fiercely, quickly, as if he wanted to own her soul as well as her body, and Larkin found herself all too willing to be swept away by the heat of his passion.

Thinking of Vladimir and the upcoming workshop had brought back all the old doubts, the old feelings of inadequacy his many infidelities had fostered. Alex, aroused and almost demonic in his desire for her, quickly brought her to a pitch of excitement that burned all thoughts of Vladimir Karpov from her mind.

Only sensation remained—pure, hot, urgent sensation as his hands first slid her panty hose off, then her silky briefs, to find her ready—more than ready—for him. He sat back on the sofa and she straddled him, arching her back, letting her hair flow over his legs. Her cashmere dress was pushed up around her waist, and he held her by her hips as she moved her body in slow, maddening circles.

She was almost oblivious of her own pleasure. What she wanted was to bring Alex to a level of sensuality he'd never known with any other woman.

Her movements grew quicker as she drew him more deeply inside her body. The muscles of his flat belly were contracting; she could feel the movement deep within.

"Tell me," she said. "Tell me what you want."

"Everything," he said. "Everything you have to give."

And so she gave him body and soul, and held on to her heart just a little longer. When she finally gave her heart to Alex, she wanted to be sure his heart was his own to give.

SO FAR IT HAD BEEN an easy night. The calls had been intelligent, witty and brief, and Alex felt he'd acquitted himself admirably. Twice Sal flashed him the thumbs-up sign after a particularly insightful answer, and Alex was delighted that he was able to come across as a rational human being, when his mind was back in Larkin's office with her astride his body, showing him a world of sensuality he'd never imagined.

He was thinking about Larkin and the upcoming visit to Phil and Judy's when he realized Sal was punching up another caller. He snapped back into gear.

"Good evening. This is Alex Jakobs and you're on *Helpline*. How can I help you?"

"Dr. Jakobs?" The male voice was raspy and forceful.

He shot a quick glance at Sal. The same apprehension he had felt the day of Karen O'Rourke's phone call settled in on him. "Speaking. How can I help you?"

"Dr. Jakobs," the voice repeated. Sal was leaning forward, watching. "Five-four-four-KHJ."

For a second Alex thought the man was speaking gibberish until it hit him: 544-KHJ was the license plate number on his Buick.

The man continued, "five-sixteen, five-five-five—"

Sal quickly cut the audio, so the public didn't hear Alex's home-phone number. The entire *Helpline* crew had learned a lot after the Karen O'Rourke episode; Sal motioned that a trace was already being ordered.

"Who are you?" he asked.

"Anyone and everyone." The man's jagged, sandy laugh sent chills up Alex's spine. "You may not believe this, Doctor, but not only the night has a thousand eyes."

The caller hung up, and Sal's muttered curse echoed in the silent studio; then he brought the audio back up.

"These things happen," Alex said calmly into the camera. He motioned for Sal to punch up another caller, and he prayed for something normal like workaholism or triskaidekaphobia to get him through until the end of the show.

When the show was finally over, Alex gratefully accepted a Scotch from Sal.

"We couldn't get the trace on him," Sal said.

Alex took a long sip and let its warmth burn down his throat. "He was too smart. He wasn't about to stay on the line long enough to be found."

Sal took a drag on his cigarette and scratched his head. "Not to worry, Doc; it's just another quack," he said. "You should be used to them in your profession."

Alex nodded. Professional disturbances he could handle. What happened tonight, however, was anything but a professional disturbance. It was personal.

Very personal.

And for some reason the memory of Gordon Franklin and the look in his eyes came to mind and stayed with Alex for the rest of the night.

THE PHONE WAS RINGING as Larkin let herself into the house a little after ten. She leaped over Amanda, who was sprawled in the doorway to the living room, and grabbed for the phone on its fourth ring.

"I can't believe it," Alex said. "I had my spiel already to give your machine."

She laughed and sank into a chair, kicking off her shoes. "The machine's in the shop. You'll have to give your spiel to a real live person."

"Not half as much fun. I was going to tell you how I felt about our interlude this afternoon."

She thought about their lovemaking, and warmth spread throughout her body. "I think that's a topic better discussed in person, don't you?"

"That's what I was hoping you'd say. Are you free tomorrow night?"

"Definitely."

"Dinner?"

"How about seven-thirty?"

He laughed. "I like a decisive woman. Any place particular in mind?"

"As long as it's not Private Eyes." She told him about her evening with Patti. "Captain Bill's was closed, so we ended up dining on hamburgers and harassment at Private Eyes. What a nightmare."

"I thought you had to be new wave and under nineteen to get in there."

"Let's just say half of the males in the room were young enough to be my son." She put her legs up on the coffee table. "I couldn't wait to make my escape."

She could hear a tinge of jealousy in Alex's voice, and it tickled her. "How long did you last in that den of thieves?"

"From the time I gave my coat to the hatcheck girl until I called a cab—it must have been all of forty-five minutes."

"Patti stayed?"

"Patti will probably close down the place," Larkin said. "I don't understand the attraction." Alex's answer was pithy and it made her blush even while she laughed. "Psychologists get right to the point, don't they?"

"Patti plays a dangerous game. I hope she's careful."

Larkin thought of Patti's determination to play the game with Vladimir Karpov, grand master of deceit. "Let's not talk about Patti," she said. "How was your show? You sound exhausted."

"I am. We had a little trouble at the studio." She listened while he told her about the phone call he'd received. "The general consensus is that it's a patient of mine."

"You don't sound convinced."

"I'm not." He stopped. Larkin had the feeling that he wanted to say more but thought better of it. "Is the house locked up for the night?"

The non sequitur threw her. "I just walked in the door as the phone rang, Alex. I'll get to all of that after."

"I'll hold on," he said firmly. "Go lock up."

She bristled. "I will after we hang up, Alex."

"Do it now, please, Larkin."

"Maybe I should just have the National Guard patrol the house while I'm at work." The joke fell short. Her annoyance, however, came through loud and clear.

"I apologize for coming on so strong," Alex said, "but I want you to be careful."

What on earth was wrong with him? He was much too levelheaded to be easily spooked. "I'm always careful."

"Then be more careful than usual."

"You're scaring me, Alex."

"You're important to me, Larkin. I care what happens to you."

"I'm a grown woman, Alex. I can take care of myself. Don't worry."

What she wanted to say was "Come to me. Take care of me," but those simple words held an even greater danger than anything Alex feared. She was better off taking a stand against intruders than handing her life over to anyone—not even to a man as wonderful as Alex Jakobs.

ALEX HUNG UP the phone.

Damn it! All day long the image of the virile Russian dancer had plagued Alex. And just now, hearing the reluctance in Larkin's voice, all his jealousies and fears rose to the surface.

He was falling in love headfirst like a foolish teenager and she was holding back, cool and distant. Sure, she had been anything but distant in his arms that afternoon, but physical passion was a thing apart.

She mistook his concern for control; that much was obvious. How could he explain the fear inside him that made him want to protect her in every way possible? How could he tell her so soon in their relationship that he could stand anything but the thought of losing her?

What Alex wanted from Larkin went way beyond what they could find in bed.

He wanted her heart and her soul as well.

THE LIGHTS DIDN'T GO OUT until nearly midnight, and then the one in the bedroom still burned.

He waited and watched, and finally it, too, was extinguished. The only light was the pinpoint from his cigarette, and he took a last drag and tossed the cigarette in a puddle near the curb. It hissed, then went out, leaving him in darkness, with only the sound of the wind and the bay beyond for company.

She was alone tonight. She was safe tonight.

He could go home. There would be other nights when she would need his protection and he had to be ready.

Chapter Fourteen

On Friday afternoon Larkin was struggling with some last-minute problems with a Chinese-cooking class when Patti burst into the room, clutching her heart.

"Don't you know how to knock?" she asked. "Alex is picking me up in three hours, and I have eight hours' more work to do."

"Pinch me!" Patti said, collapsing on the sofa.

"I'll do more than pinch you if you don't tell me what's going on."

"He's on the phone!"

"Who?" Larkin asked, although she had a pretty good idea.

"Vladimir-rrr!" Patti rolled the *r* in perfect imitation of his Russian accent. "He vants to speak vit you."

The pencil in Larkin's hand began to shake and she quickly put it down. "What about? We sent his publicist all the material on the workshop." She took a deep breath, trying to control her nerves. "Maybe you could help him, Patti."

"You bet I could. Unfortunately, right now he wants you. I told him you were busy, but that man is insistent." She sighed. "I like a man who knows what he wants."

"You just like men, Patti." She took off her right earring and waited until Patti left the room before she picked up the phone.

"Larkin Walker speaking."

"How businesslike, Larkin Walker." No one else on earth sounded like Vladimir Karpov. Her name on his lips sent a tremor through her body that was impossible to control even now. Even after so much.

"Vladimir?" How calm and collected she sounded. She deserved an Oscar *and* an Emmy for this performance. "It's been a long time."

"Thirty-three months—and I count the days until the twenty-ninth. How many times I have pictured you."

"You flatter me, Vladimir. And here I thought I was just a pleasant memory."

"Never that." His voice was low and intimate. "The time I spent with you was—"

"Where are you calling from?" she broke in. "I thought you were in London right now."

"So I am. I will be flying into Kennedy Airport tomorrow."

Her heart dropped to her stomach. "Why?"

"A benefit dinner for artistic freedom."

"How nice."

"Even nicer if you would be my guest."

"Sorry, I'll be out of town."

Patti was standing in the doorway, her blue eyes wide and fastened securely on Larkin.

"All of the old guard will be there," Vladimir said, his voice growing more persuasive. "I remember how you used to shine above all—"

"Impossible," Larkin said. "Thank you for asking, but I can't make it."

"Plans can be changed."

"Not these plans."

"You sound quite American these days, my love."

"If by that you mean independent, I am."

"I think I like you this way."

Patti was sitting on the edge of Larkin's desk now, but Larkin ignored her. "I don't care if you like me this way or not, Vladimir. It doesn't matter to me at all."

"And where is it you're going that's so important to you that you break my heart?"

"Virginia."

"Fox hunting?"

She certainly wasn't about to say that she was attending a six-year-old's birthday party. "Alex and I just felt like flying down for the weekend."

"And who is this Alex? Someone you conjure up to make me sorry?"

"Now you flatter yourself, Vladimir." Patti was almost falling into her lap with curiosity.

"You have not told me who this Alex is, my love."

"Very perceptive of you."

"There is nothing I can do to change your mind?"

"Absolutely nothing."

"You are very different, Larkin. I can see things have changed for you."

"You were responsible for much of that, Vladimir." She could never be that naive, that eager to please again. Her self-respect wouldn't allow it.

"I am not certain I like the change."

"That is your problem, Vladimir, not mine." She paused. "Now, if there's nothing else . . ."

"There are many things, my love, but they can wait until the twenty-ninth. I am not as certain that I can, though. Au revoir."

He was gone.

Larkin slammed the receiver down on the console. "Damn! I don't know why in hell I let him get under my skin like that."

Patti jumped up from the desk and sat on the couch, a respectable distance away from Larkin's wrath. "I want to say he can get under my skin anytime, but something tells me I shouldn't."

"Not if you value your job."

"What did this man say to you? You look like you're considering mayhem."

"Mayhem would be too good for him. After all these years, he still thinks my world should grind to a halt just because he wants it to."

"So I gathered. Where did he want to take you?"

"Some benefit dinner—who knows if it even exists? I've just floated back into his line of vision again, and he's hoping to arrange for some excitement while he's in town."

"Give him my phone number. I can arrange for some excitement."

"You haven't heard a word I've said, have you?"

"Yes, I have. It's just that we're very different—you're looking for forever after. I'll settle for one great night."

"You deserve more than one great night, Patti. Why can't you believe that?"

The laughter fell away from Patti, and Larkin saw a vulnerability in her eyes much like that in Gordon's. "Because then it doesn't hurt so much when that's all I get."

"Stay away from him, Patti," Larkin said, putting her arm around her. "Please."

Patti met her eyes. "Are you asking me, Larkin, or telling me?"

"Neither, Patti. I'm just trying to help you."

Patti's old insouciance returned. "Well, if you really want to help me, let me be his liaison while he's in town."

"Sorry, Patti. You're on your own. I may not be able to stop you, but I'll be damned if I deliver you to him on a silver platter."

"Don't you worry," Patti said with a grin. "I intend to deliver myself to him, gift-wrapped."

"Not on company time. I'm not going to pay you to get your heart broken."

Patti laughed and headed for the door. "Have no fear, Larkin. My heart's safe."

Brave words.

Larkin only wished she could make the same statement.

WHILE LARKIN WAS WRESTLING with some serious questions, Alex was in the toy store doing the same thing.

The salesclerk showed Alex a red-haired Cabbage Patch Kid and waited for his reaction.

"It's still ugly," Alex said. "Are you sure this is what six-year-olds like?"

The woman looked at him smugly. "You don't have children, do you, sir?"

Alex shook his head.

"Believe me, these dolls are all the rage."

"I thought that was a few Christmases ago. Haven't they moved on to something else?"

The saleswoman arched a well-tended brow. "Unless you opt for a big-ticket item like a furnished dollhouse, this is top-of-the-line." She glanced at the adoption certificate. "I'm sure the birthday girl will fall in love with Callie Josephine."

"Callie Josephine?"

"That's what the adoption papers say. Of course, the adoptive mother can always request a name change."

This was an area of weirdness they hadn't covered in graduate school. "I'm just not sure."

Suddenly the salesclerk's eyes lit up. She hurried into the storeroom and returned with a large box behind her back. "The pièce de résistance," she said. "Twins!"

There, looking up at him, their chubby faces mirror images of one another, were Margie Lorraine and Rachel Ann. He started to laugh. This was fantasy carried to the extreme, but he was beginning to see how a little child's imagination could take flight.

"Brand-new item," the salesclerk said. "She'll be the first little girl on Long Island with twins."

"The first little girl in Fairfax, Virginia," he said. He thought of Cameron and the vivid stories she wove about her dolls and stuffed animals—intricate, detailed stories that made him wonder just how much a child was capable of achieving. What she couldn't do with twins! He pulled out his American Express card. "Margie and Rachel," he said, "you're coming with me."

The saleswoman beamed like an obstetrician after a particularly easy delivery. "A wonderful choice," she said. "I know the girls will be very happy in Virginia. We've placed many of the dolls in out-of-state adoptions."

Alex couldn't resist. He looked at the woman and said, "They don't get airsick, do they?"

LARKIN WAS LAUGHING so hard that tears ran down her cheeks. She'd made Alex repeat his statement twice, and she still found it impossible to believe. "She didn't! Tell me you're lying, Alex, please!"

"It's true," Alex said. "She told me to give each a half-dose of Dramamine before boarding the plane."

Larkin started laughing all over again, holding her sides. "She didn't even crack a smile?"

Alex pulled into the airport parking lot and took his reserved spot. "Not even a little one. Adoption is serious business, Larkin."

"And here I thought Ken and Barbie were a hot item when I was growing up," she said as they unloaded the car of suitcases and presents.

Larkin had purchased a small electric train set for Cameron, not as a determinedly nonsexist statement, but because she remembered the tremendous pleasure she'd experienced playing with her brothers' trains as a little girl.

Jayne, who had called Larkin minutes before Alex picked her up at the office, had been appalled.

"Honey, just because you like to play with trains doesn't mean every little girl does."

"Don't worry, Mom," she'd said with a laugh. "Don't Billy's daughters love his old train set?"

"That's different," Jayne said. "You want to make the right impression on Judy and Phil."

"No, Mom. I want to make Cameron happy. Judy and Phil can buy their own electric trains."

"Larkin!"

"Mother!"

Larkin knew her mother had been truly horrified. Jayne viewed the trip to Virginia to meet the Lincolns as Alex's equivalent of taking Larkin home to meet his family, and she had been obviously dismayed that her daughter didn't view it the same way.

The truth was that the week had been so busy at the Center that Larkin hadn't had time to analyze Alex's motives. Then Vladimir's phone call had unnerved her so much that it was all she could do to finish work and get home in time to shower and change.

But now, as she watched Alex go through his preflight routine, she began to wonder if perhaps her mother wasn't right. Phil and Judy were his oldest friends. Hadn't he said it had always been Phil-and-Judy-and-Alex-and Rikki? The invitation to Cameron's birthday party went way beyond sharing cake and cookies with a houseful of six-year-olds. It was a way of sharing the most personal parts of his life with her.

Larkin's stomach suddenly tightened up, and she wondered if Margie Lorraine and Rachel Ann would share their Dramamine with her.

ALEX HAD MADE THIS TRIP countless times in the past ten years, but it wasn't until he turned onto Fox Hollow Court and headed toward Phil and Judy's house that it hit him. Larkin was the first person with whom he'd shared this part of his life.

He had called Phil and Judy six times in the past three days, telling them what Larkin liked to drink, her favorite foods—right down to the infamous chocolate-chip cookies—her taste in music. Phil teased him mercilessly, and even Judy got in some lighthearted needling. Alex knew he was acting like a love-struck high school kid but, dammit, he couldn't help it.

He glanced over at Larkin. She sat beside him, humming softly along with the radio, looking more beautiful than any mortal woman had the right to look. Her long amber hair was piled loosely on top of her head, accentuating the classic loveliness of her profile.

"Their house is the last one on the right side," he said. "The two-story brick."

"The old one with the big oak tree in front?"

"Fantastic, isn't it? It was built just after the turn of the century."

"What a wonderful home to raise a family in. No wonder you love to visit."

Alex was a man who believed in ritual and tradition, a man without family who had created the family he needed with these old and dear friends. Phil and Judy and their children would always be an important part of his life.

Now, more than ever, he hoped Larkin would be, as well.

He had forgotten how much joy life had to offer, and he was anxious to make up for lost time.

JUDY LINCOLN WAS BRUNETTE, petite and disarmingly direct. Larkin liked her on first sight.

"You're a brave woman, Larkin," Judy said after they were introduced. "I don't know if I'd travel six hundred miles to attend a six-year-old's birthday party."

"Alex is a very persuasive man," Larkin said. "Besides, I have seven nieces and nephews of my own. Sometimes I actually miss being around children."

"A live one," Phil said with a manic grin. "You pack, Judy. I'll start the car. We can reach the state line by sundown."

"He's only kidding," Alex said, plunking their overnight bags down in the center hall of the Lincolns' big colonial house. "There's nothing Phil loves more than his kids."

Judy coughed politely. "Aren't you forgetting something, Alex?"

Alex slapped his forehead with the palm of his hand. "Of course! There's nothing Phil loves more than his kids and his '59 Caddy."

Larkin's eyes widened. Her father was a car buff, and she knew all about the '59 Caddy, with razor-sharp fins that went on forever. "Don't tell me you have a '59 Caddy!"

"Okay, I won't," Phil said, slipping his arm through hers. "How about I show you instead?"

And just that easily she felt welcomed into Alex's family, for that was what Phil, Judy and their children were to Alex. Coming down to Virginia for Cameron's birthday party had been the perfect opportunity to introduce Larkin to the people he cared most about in the world. That these people had been Rikki's friends as well was not lost on her.

The kids came home from school at four and Larkin loved the way they adored Alex. The evening was filled with talk of Caddies and birthday balloons and with dinner and dancing at the club Phil and Judy belonged to. The four of them got back to the house around midnight and settled down in the den.

What a delight it was to watch Alex with old friends, to see the lines of worry and fatigue smoothed over, to hear him trade jokes with people he'd known much of his life.

Rikki came up in the conversation once or twice, but it had been such a natural part of the exchange that Larkin didn't feel the slightest pang—well, maybe the tiniest of pangs, but nothing she couldn't handle.

"Don't you go believing this three-piece-suit routine of Alex's," Phil was saying as Judy brought another pot of coffee into the den. "He was as tough as they come, back in high school." He turned to Alex, who was sprawled in front of the fireplace, trying to assemble the electric train set for Cameron. "How many times did you get kicked out for cutting class?"

Alex looked up, met Larkin's eyes and smiled in a way that set her pulses leaping. "I stopped counting after the eleventh suspension. I wasn't what you would call motivated back in those days."

Larkin winked at Phil and Judy. "And here I thought you were a boy genius, head bent forever over your schoolwork."

"Sorry to disappoint you, but I had 'trouble' written all over me."

"But you seem so levelheaded." She glanced at Phil, whose red hair appeared to have a life of its own. "Now, if you told me Phil was a problem kid, that I could believe."

Judy's boisterous laugh rang out. "Phil was a Goody Two-Shoes," she said, ruffling her husband's wild mop of hair. "Alex and I used to work overtime thinking of ways to loosen Phil and Rikki up."

It was probably the three glasses of wine she had had with dinner, coupled with being premenstrual, but when Judy started reminiscing about the time she and Alex nailed Rikki's sneakers to the floor of the gymnasium, Larkin excused herself to phone home for messages. It wasn't jealousy she was feeling, but a sorrow so deep that it almost robbed her of speech.

"Use the phone in my room," Judy said. "The one in the den has a tendency to disconnect you."

Their voices faded as Larkin climbed the stairs to the master bedroom. A brass lamp burned softly on the nightstand by the phone, and she sat on the edge of the bed and dialed her number. She was waiting for the machine to pick up so she could dial in her code when she noticed it.

There, right next to the clock radio, was a photo in a wooden frame. A young Phil and Judy beamed out at the camera, holding a hand-lettered Just Married sign in front of them. However, it was the couple next to them that drew Larkin's eye and held it. Alex, beardless and painfully thin, stood with his arm around a beautiful redhead who looked up at him as if he held the secrets to the universe in the palm of his hand.

No one had to tell Larkin that the red-haired woman was Erika Lewin Jakobs. They looked so right together, so totally and perfectly in sync with each other that Larkin quickly put the picture down as if it were radioactive.

No one had to tell her that if Rikki were still alive, Larkin wouldn't stand a chance.

WHEN LARKIN DIDN'T COME DOWN in a half hour, Alex said good-night to Phil and Judy and went upstairs. He found her, fully clothed, on the double bed in the darkened guest bedroom.

"Are you all right?" He felt his way to the edge of the bed and sat down.

"Just tired." She kissed his hand as he brushed a strand of hair off her cheek. "It hit me all of a sudden."

He reached to turn on the lamp, but she stopped him.

"Are you sure our walk down memory lane isn't what put you to sleep?"

She was quiet for a moment; then she said, "I saw a picture of Rikki in Phil and Judy's bedroom. She was beautiful."

His throat tightened. "Yes, she was."

"You must miss her terribly."

"I did for a long time," he said. "Now I miss what could have been more than what once was." Family occasions like

Cameron's birthday usually served to underscore the basic human experiences that had been denied him. This time, however, having Larkin by his side made all the difference. That hard shell of loneliness didn't stand a chance against her warmth and generosity.

He pulled his shoes off and lay down next to her on the narrow bed. Other nights, on other visits, he'd lain in this bed and wondered how it would have been if Rikki had lived, if it were their children asleep down the hall, bathed in the glow of a Mickey Mouse night-light.

Tonight, however, was different. He wanted to talk about the past and put it behind him. He wanted to build something with Larkin, something fine and strong—something that would last a lifetime, however long or short that lifetime was.

"Sometimes it feels like another lifetime," he said into the darkness, "as if it all happened to someone else." The memories were still strong, but the sharp edges of pain mercifully had dulled.

"Seeing her made it so real for me," Larkin said, her voice soft against his cheek. "You seemed so happy, so in love."

"We were." Iconoclastic children of the sixties who eschewed materialism and embraced solid middle-class values of marital fidelity. "Ironic, isn't it?"

"Very." Her voice cracked, and he felt tears against his skin.

"Don't cry," he said—stupid, inane words. Why shouldn't she cry? All the promises made in the heat of the night didn't matter a damn before the hand of fate.

He held Larkin close, and the thought occurred to him that perhaps she cried for more than Rikki, for more than the pain her death had caused him. Perhaps Larkin thought of Vladimir Karpov and felt his loss as keenly as Alex felt the loss of his wife.

They knew so much about each other, so many of the nuts-and-bolts facts of their lives. He had exposed more of his soul to Larkin than to anyone—even to Rikki. With Rikki he had needed to be strong, to protect her, to provide for her. Rikki had been a capable woman, but their marriage had been a traditional one. Larkin's independence seemed as intrinsic to her as the beauty she carried so easily around her like a shield. She was strong enough to handle the fact that even well-known psychologists sometimes needed a shoulder to lean upon.

Not once had she given him any insight into what made her the woman she was. Conditioning and genetics both played a part; her independence, however, seemed too highly prized to be a circumstance of birth.

Alex's relationship with Rikki had gone a long way toward shaping him into the man he was today.

He had the feeling Vladimir Karpov was somehow responsible for the woman Larkin Walker was. The well-known psychologist didn't quite know what to make of that fact.

Chapter Fifteen

As usual, Larkin kicked off her shoes the second she stepped inside.

"Pure bliss." She flashed him a smile. "Just leave the suitcase in the hall, Alex. I'll worry about it later."

"I'll put it in the bedroom, if you'll start some coffee for us."

"Why didn't I think of that? The smell of Judy's chocolate-chip cookies has been driving me crazy since we left Virginia."

How good it was to be back home. If there was anything Larkin had learned in the last month, it was that old relationships exerted a pull that went on much, much longer than she'd ever believed. She had only to think of her own reaction to Vladimir's voice on the telephone Friday to know just how true that was.

She flipped the light switch in the kitchen and poured bottled water into the coffee maker. Friday night she and Alex had soothed each other with their bodies in an attempt to push back the memories that seemed to leap out at every turn. On Saturday they threw themselves into the frenzied activity surrounding Cameron's birthday party by day and, once again, sought oblivion together by night.

Larkin loved being with Phil and Judy; however, she had been keenly aware of her status as an outsider. What existed between her and Alex seemed as tenuous as the wrappings on Cameron's birthday presents.

In the intimate darkness of the plane ride back from Virginia, Alex had tried to bring the conversation around to weightier matters, but each time, Larkin deftly turned the subject back to her plans for Thanksgiving dinner and how much she hoped Phil and Judy could join them. How much easier it was to talk about dinner menus than what was really on her mind.

The temptation to give in and let love happen was powerful, but the need to protect herself, even more so. Endings hurt—both she and Alex had had firsthand experience of that. And now Vladimir was about to reenter her life and give her a refresher course on exactly how it felt to be second-best.

THE BEDROOM WAS DARK. Alex pushed the wall switch up with his elbow, then put the suitcase down on the stand near the armoire. His shoulders were tight from the accumulated tensions of both flying and driving, and he stretched his arms overhead, his knuckles grazing the smooth, pale surface of the ceiling.

The weekend with Phil and Judy had been a success, but once again Alex was aware that his relationship with Larkin was out of balance.

He'd seen her intelligence, felt her passion, dried her tears. But there was still a part of her that stayed out of reach.

The past few days had brought certain facts home to him in a way he could no longer ignore. He wanted to be married; he wanted a home and family; he wanted to share who and what he was with the woman he loved. Larkin was willing to think as far ahead as Thanksgiving; he wanted to think about the rest of their lives.

INSTEAD OF dissipating the tension that had been growing between them all evening, the act of lovemaking increased it. The atmosphere in Larkin's bedroom crackled with it despite hours of intense pleasure.

She leaned on one elbow and let her long hair float across his bare chest. "What was in those cookies Judy gave us? Is it something only Virginians know about, or can we Northerners get in on it?"

He said nothing, simply pulled her down until her breasts were flattened against his chest and her lips rested on his.

"This is all very flattering, Alex," she murmured with a laugh, "but I wouldn't be at all offended if we called a time-out."

His hands spanned her waist, and he moved against her. "Still think I should call a time-out?" His breath was hot against the side of her throat.

"You're amazing. And here I thought that men reached their sexual peak at nineteen."

"A vicious rumor," he said, moving in a way that stole her breath, "spread by overanxious young boys."

"Apparently there's still life at thirty-six."

He entered her and she gasped. "Apparently there is."

Once again they made love, and once again the level of tension between them increased. Afterward they lay side by side in her bed, and she watched as a series of emotions flickered across his face. She saw in his eyes the same confusion she had been feeling all weekend.

"Alex? Is something wrong?" It was a dangerous question, but one she had to ask.

"I was going to ask you the same thing."

Their faces were inches apart. His eyes met hers, and there was no place to hide.

She took a deep breath. "We're a little off balance tonight, aren't we?"

"We've been off balance all weekend, Larkin."

She couldn't deny it. "I shouldn't have let the picture of Rikki throw me like that. I'm sorry. It's just being with your friends, seeing how large a part of your life Rikki was, well, I—"

"It's more than that."

"It is?" What on earth was he getting at?

"Anyone would feel the way you felt seeing Rikki's photo. I want to know why I feel the same way about Vladimir Karpov."

She wanted to get up and leave the bed, but his gaze held her captive. "I don't know why you're feeling that way, Alex. There's no reason to."

"Are you sure?"

She laughed. "Of course I'm sure. Vladimir and I were lovers a few years ago, but that's long over."

"But you've remained friends."

"Is that so unusual?"

He paused a moment. "I have a feeling that in this case it is."

"Perhaps you should leave your Ph.D. at the bedroom door next time, Alex." She couldn't disguise the edge in her voice. He was coming too close to a painful subject. "This is hardly the time for impromptu analysis."

"I don't want to analyze you," he said. "I want to love you."

A tremor began deep inside. "You've done that quite well already—several times, actually."

"That was making love, Larkin."

"I don't understand the distinction."

"I think you do." His hand cupped her chin and raised her face so that she was forced to look at him. "What's happening between us is a hell of a lot more than just physical attraction."

"I don't think this is the time for a philosophical discussion, Alex." One hand slid low on his body. "I'm sure we could find a better time for that."

He grasped her wrist. "When?"

"I don't know," she said, exasperated. "Tomorrow afternoon at three twenty-three. What kind of question is that?"

"A logical one," he shot back. "In case you haven't noticed, we seem to have a problem getting together during the week."

"We managed the other day to get together."

She could see that he remembered the incredible interlude in her office.

"Sex is important, Larkin, but I'm ready to take the next step."

"We haven't known each other that long, Alex. We have plenty of time ahead of us."

"Can you guarantee that?"

She thought of Rikki. "No, I can't."

He traced the outline of her mouth with the tip of one finger. "Are you ready to hear what I want to say to you?"

I'm not, she thought. *I'm not ready to let myself believe.* She was unable, however, to say the words aloud.

"Talk to me," he said. "Tell me what made you the woman you are."

"Isn't it enough that we're here together?" How difficult he was making this. "You want to talk about your past, but I simply don't have the need to talk about mine." She wasn't proud of the woman she had been with Vladimir and was not about to share that humiliation with Alex, no matter how much she was growing to love him.

He pulled her to him in an embrace so intense that it drove logic and fear from her brain.

"I'll give you more time," he said fiercely. His heart pounded against her breast as he moved his hand against her in a movement so voluptuous that she cried out. "But I want more than this." He slid inside her and she caught and held him fast. "I want everything you have, Larkin, and I'll give you up before I settle for anything less."

She had to struggle to keep the words "I love you" tucked safely inside her heart.

AS ALEX DROVE HOME that night, still warm from her bed, he struggled with the realization that Karpov was the key to the reluctant lover he had held in his arms.

Two weeks from now, Karpov would be back in her life, and she would have the opportunity to compare both men. What Alex wanted more than anything was to spirit her away in his Cessna to some far-off island where he could drive every last memory of the dancer from her mind, where he could take possession of her heart the way he took possession of her body each time they were together.

Alex knew he would never give her up. There was no power in heaven or hell that could make him willingly turn away from the miracle he'd found with Larkin Walker.

He'd promised to give her time, time to sort out her feelings, time to take a step closer to him. Time, however, could also work against him, and his thoughts so occupied his mind that he didn't notice the figure crouched at the foot of his driveway or the pungent smell of burning wood until he saw the flames—red and yellow—flickering over the roof of his house.

"YOU'RE A LUCKY MAN, Mr. Jakobs." The detective popped the cap back on his pen and looked at Alex. "A busted roof and some smoke damage in the den. You could've lost everything."

Alex, covered with soot and ash, looked at the man as if he were crazy. "Lucky men don't have cranks setting fire to their homes, Detective Venitelli."

Venitelli stuffed his notebook and pen into the pocket of his overcoat. "There's no sign of arson, no forced entry."

"What about the dead birds last week?"

"Birds die, Mr. Jakobs. Nothing so unusual about that."

"Birds don't die on your front door with chains around their necks."

Venitelli grinned and looked as if he were about to crack a joke, but Alex's expression obviously stopped him cold. "I made a note about that. We'll check into it, but don't expect nothing from it."

"I expect an investigation."

Venitelli arched a brow. "You got any ideas who's behind this? In your line of work you probably meet a lot of wackos who aren't too happy paying your fancy prices."

The man was a fool. "I told you about the episode during last week's program."

Venitelli nodded. "Yeah, yeah. The guy with your license number. Not too much to go on."

"Sorry," Alex snapped, "my sleuthing skills are a little rusty." He toyed with idea of mentioning Gordon Franklin, but Venitelli had the sensitivity of an armadillo. Unless Alex caught Gordon planting a pipe bomb under his car, Alex's vague suspicions wouldn't count a damn with the detective.

He thought of Larkin in her house by the water, and he had to fight down the urge to call her to reassure himself of her safety.

Absurd. *His* house was the one set on fire. *He* was the one receiving strange phone calls and even stranger messages on his doorstep. A practicing therapist with a TV show had every reason to expect the occasional crackpot to cross his path. There was no logical reason for him to tie Larkin in with this in any way, shape or form. And yet the look on Gordon Franklin's face in the reception room of the Learning Center a few weeks ago still lingered with Alex.

Sleep that night was a long time coming.

LARKIN COVERED the mouthpiece of the telephone and whispered thanks as Patti deposited a sheaf of advertising material on her desk. "Yes, I'm still here, Mom. Patti just brought in some papers." Jayne had wanted all the details on Larkin's weekend in Virginia with the Lincolns.

"Say hi to Jayne for me," Patti called out, loud enough for Jayne to hear her without benefit of AT&T.

Larkin handed the phone to Patti. "Here. Say hi yourself." Her mother was crazy about the flamboyant Patti Franklin. Last Thanksgiving Jayne and Patti had entertained everyone with a version of "One" from *A Chorus Line* that Roger still talked about.

Patti laughed her usual boisterous laugh and handed the phone back to Larkin a few minutes later. "We're going to do a scene from *Grease* this year."

"I hope that's not a comment on my cooking."

Still laughing, Patti left the room.

"Do I have to dust off my poodle skirt?" Larkin asked her mother.

"You just worry about the turkey," Jayne said. "Patricia and I will provide the entertainment." Jayne paused for effect. "Do you think your Alex is ready for us?"

"Is that your way of asking if he's invited?"

"I'm trying to be subtle, honey. I thought you'd appreciate it."

"He claims to be a whiz in the kitchen, and he said he'd provide the chestnut dressing and the pies."

"If he's anything like your father and brothers, he'll ask for a little help from Pepperidge Farm and Sara Lee."

"He's nothing like any of them. He does dishes. In fact, he's cooking dinner for me tonight at his house."

"Hold on to him. Men like that are hard to find."

Larkin couldn't resist. "Maybe you should mention this to Dad. I don't think he's too old to learn the mysteries of lemon-scented Joy."

"We're getting off track," Jayne said, letting Larkin's remark pass. "You never did tell me if you had a good time with Alex's friends or not."

"They're wonderful people," Larkin said. "Judy has relatives in Brooklyn, and I told her to drop by on Thanksgiving if they have a chance."

"You didn't answer my question."

"I was hoping you hadn't noticed."

"I'm your mother," Jayne said. "I notice everything."

"I saw a picture of Rikki on the nightstand in Judy's room. It didn't do much for my mood."

"Why do I get the feeling there's more to this than you're telling me?"

Because you're my mother, Larkin thought. *Because you always know when something troubles me.* "I think your ESP is working overtime, Mom," she said easily. "Cam's birthday party was a smashing success."

"You've heard from Vladimir Karpov, haven't you?"

"I think you should leave your brain to science, Mom. This is getting too spooky for me."

"I wish you didn't have to see him again. Patricia is perfectly capable of handling the workshop series on her own."

"The Center is my responsibility, Mom, not Patti's."

"You're not still in love with him, are you?"

"Of course not." Larkin felt attracted to him, intrigued by him, betrayed by him, but she definitely was not in love with him. "I haven't been for a very long time."

"He can be a very charming man, honey. When he—"

Despite herself Larkin began to laugh. "Mom, I'm the one who lived with him for two years." *Two years, three months and sixteen days.* "I know all about how charming he can be."

"I worry about you, honey. You've managed to turn your life around—I'd hate to see Vladimir do anything to upset things with your Alex Jakobs."

"You worry way too much," she said, ignoring the truth in her mother's words. "And besides, he's not *my* Alex Jakobs. Now let's forget about men and concentrate on Thanksgiving."

Easier said than done. Her mother's words lingered with her for hours afterward. All Larkin wanted out of Vladimir's affiliation with the Center was publicity and the chance to show him what she had accomplished with her life. Let Patti fall prey to his charm. Larkin believed that she was immune and intended to stay that way.

"WHAT ARE YOU DOING here?" Larkin, in spangled red-white-and-blue leotard and tights, seemed shocked to see him. "You're supposed to be home cooking dinner for me."

"Change of plans," Alex said, drawing her into his arms and kissing her. He explained about the fire the night before and reassured her that he was fine. "The house stinks from smoke, and the workmen have been at it all day."

He sat down on the couch in her office and grinned as she began doing some warm-up exercises before her advanced tap-dancing class began.

"You should have called," she said, stretching one leg back and up in an impossibly graceful gesture. "I would have met you at a restaurant."

The truth was that he'd hoped to bump into Gordon Franklin while he was there and put his suspicions to rest. "I have a better idea. Give me the keys to your house and I'll have dinner waiting there when you get home."

She was flat on the floor now in a yoga posture. "I have some soup in the freezer."

"When I promise a woman dinner, I deliver. The groceries are in my car: Cornish hens, wild rice, chocolate mousse cake—"

"Stop right there!" She sat up. "Chocolate mousse cake from Dietz's Bakery?"

"A large one."

She reached up for her house keys on top of her desk and handed them to him. "My kitchen is a mess, Alex. If you have any problems, call Roger. He's home until seven-thirty."

He kissed the top of her head, and the scent of her perfume blossomed around him. "I'm a whiz in the kitchen," he said, relishing the lovely curves of her body as she assumed another exotic pose. "If you have a stove, a mixing bowl and a knife, I'll be fine."

"You know, my mother's beginning to think you're the perfect man."

He grinned. Progress—she'd told her mother about him. "I promise not to do anything to change her mind when I meet her at Thanksgiving." The thing to do now was convince Larkin that he was the perfect man.

He walked her downstairs to the enormous rehearsal hall, where the strangest assortment of neophyte tap dancers limbered up in the hallway: a woman in a chartreuse running suit, an elderly man with polished tap shoes, even a young girl in top hat and tails—and they were the conservative ones.

"I'll be home by eight," Larkin said, "tired, cranky and starving." She kissed his cheek. "I just want to give you fair warning."

"I'll leave the chocolate mousse cake on the doorstep," he said. "That should soothe your savage soul."

He lingered a few moments, then headed back upstairs. Classes on how to balance a checkbook and safe travel for cowardly tourists filled the first-floor hallway with laughter and conversation that probably did more for the human condition than anything he'd learned in graduate school. Somehow Larkin had managed to parlay the basic need for companionship and knowledge into a thriving business that gave as much as it got.

He was deep in thought about this woman he loved when Gordon popped out of the storeroom near the lobby.

His response was casual and light. "Hello, Gordon. We're going to have to stop meeting like this."

To his surprise the young man maintained eye contact and smiled back. "They better install that stoplight you talked about last time before we have an accident."

"We'll have to petition the county."

Gordon nodded and retreated down the corridor, disappearing through the door leading to the garage outside.

Alex had expected anger; he saw a smile instead. He had expected anxiety; he saw a young man at ease with himself. None of the rage or jealousy so obvious on Gordon's face before was visible today.

He was glad he hadn't mentioned his suspicions either to the police detective or to Larkin. After speaking with Gordon, they would have wondered about Alex's sanity. Venitelli was probably right: some *Helpline* viewer had found Alex's TV psychotherapy to be lacking and was expressing his or her displeasure in a very melodramatic manner.

Alex forced all negative thoughts from his mind as he headed across the parking lot to his car. He was sick of thinking about it.

Let Venitelli worry about the fire and the doorstep offerings and the phone calls in the night.

Alex had more important things to do.

He had a beautiful woman to woo and win.

THE HEAVY DOOR CLOSED behind him with a loud thud. He leaned against it and fought for breath; his heart pumped so fast and hard that he thought he would pass out.

But his adrenaline also pumped fast and hard, and the elation streaking through him made him feel invincible.

How easy it had been to smile and nod and watch suspicion and doubt vanish from the man's face. The man hadn't even noticed the burn that ran red and angry down his right forearm, testimony to his actions the night before. How easy it was going to be when the time came to tell her how he felt.

She would have no choice but to be his.

Chapter Sixteen

"Honey, he's gorgeous."

Larkin looked up from basting the turkey and smiled at her mother. "Twenty-seven pounds, three ounces." She closed the oven door. "I don't dare mention the price."

"I didn't mean the turkey."

"Somehow I didn't think so."

"He and your father hit it off right away. They're out there watching the Jets like old friends."

"Dad would watch football with anyone, Mom. I've seen him pull people off the streets to watch a game with him."

"You know what I'm talking about, Larkin."

Larkin certainly did. From the moment Jayne and Bill Walker arrived at Larkin's house late last night, Jayne had been singing Alex's praises to anyone who would listen.

For the past two weeks Alex had been wooing Larkin with an intensity that made it hard for her to sleep at night for thinking of how wonderful a shared future might be. Obviously, Jayne found him beyond reproach. Larkin would have to bring her mother back down to earth in short order before Jayne announced her daughter's engagement at the dinner table.

"Alex *is* a wonderful man, Mom, but he doesn't walk on water."

"Who doesn't walk on water?"

Alex lounged in the entrance to the kitchen with two empty beer steins dangling from his hands.

"Mom was just giving me a Bible lesson," Larkin said, relishing the flush on her mother's cheeks. "She said you—"

Jayne kicked her only daughter in the ankle.

"You look thirsty," Jayne said, taking the empty steins from Alex. "Go back to the game. I'll bring you refills."

The smile he gave her mother was so warm and open Larkin was almost jealous.

"You keep doing what you're doing," he said, opening the refrigerator and taking out two bottles of beer. "I know where everything is."

Jayne refused to hand over the steins. "I won't hear of it. Go back to your game. Men and football go together on Thanksgiving."

"Just like women and housework," Larkin muttered under her breath, to Alex's amusement.

Jayne poured beer into the steins.

"You spoil men rotten," Larkin said. "It's no wonder Daddy never lets you out of his sight."

"Is that how it seems to you?"

"That's how it is, isn't it?"

Her mother just smiled. Alex, leaning against the doorjamb, seemed to be absorbing every nuance of conversation like a human sponge.

There was no time, however, to contemplate the intricacies of her parents' marriage. There was a salad to make, sweet potatoes to prepare and a thousand other details to take care of before Patti and Gordon and Roger and Kurt and—maybe—the Lincolns arrived. All that, and she still had to make herself beautiful.

"No one stays in this kitchen without working," she said to Alex. "Either go back to the den or pitch in."

Jayne stared at her.

"Don't look at me like that, Mom. Guests will be arriving in less than an hour, and I still have to shower and change and make up my face and—"

Her mother pushed her toward the door. "Go do it then, honey. I'll hold down the fort."

"I can't leave you two—"

Alex took his place at the worktable. "Go," he said. "I'm an able-bodied man. I can handle kitchen detail."

Larkin looked at her mother, but Jayne's face betrayed no hint of intrigue. It was risky, leaving her mother alone in the kitchen with a handsome, single doctor who walked on water, but it was a risk she had to take.

"Have fun," she said, grabbing a stein of beer to give to her father. "I'm going to go get dressed."

She tried to ignore the look on her mother's face as she left the room.

For Alex it was love at first sight. Not only was Jayne Walker as beautiful as her daughter, she was one of the kindest, most delightful human beings he had ever met. Even a 21-21 football game, with the Jets holding the ball at the five-yard line, wasn't enough to compete with the pleasure of her company.

"You really should go in and watch the game," Jayne said as she peeled some potatoes. "I think I can hold down the fort while Larkin changes."

"I still haven't forgiven the Jets for moving to New Jersey. Besides, it looks as if you could use a little help on KP." He grabbed a knife and started peeling potatoes.

"You really do know your way around the kitchen, don't you?"

"It was either learn to cook or depend on frozen pizza the rest of my life." He quartered a potato, tossed it in a bowl and grabbed another one. "And since I enjoy eating as much as I do, there was really no choice." He grinned at her. "You seem surprised."

"I'm not surprised, I'm enchanted. I told Larkin that if you did dishes, you were the perfect man."

"Semiperfect. At home I rely on paper plates."

"I'm glad. Perfect people are so boring." She left the potatoes to him and started trimming broccoli.

"I'm looking forward to your tap-dance extravaganza later. Patti told me you're choreographing one of the old Rockette routines."

Jayne grimaced. "I had to tone down those kicks a little. They can be rough going."

Alex looked at Larkin's mother. Fifty-eight years old she might be, but he had no doubt she could handle any routine imaginable. "I don't think you'd have any trouble at all."

Her laugh delighted him. "Not me, honey. I was worried about Patti and Larkin. All that desk work has made those two girls soft."

Alex reached for another potato. He wasn't sure that Larkin needed fourteen pounds of potatoes to go with dinner, but he had no desire to relinquish Jayne's company. "You know, there's something about your daughter I've been wondering about."

"Perhaps you should ask her. Larkin is fanatic about maintaining her privacy."

"It's something only you can answer."

Jayne put down her paring knife and looked at him, her eyes as green and as lovely as her daughter's. "I'll try."

"Where on earth did she get the name Larkin?" He'd expected Jayne to laugh at the question. She didn't. "Have I crossed some boundary I shouldn't have?"

"No, nothing like that." Jayne brushed some of her pale blond hair off her face. "Larkin was my last name before I married Bill."

"I see. You wanted to carry it on. Family tradition."

"No. I wanted to *start* a family tradition. Larkin was the last name they gave me at the orphanage where I grew up.

The truck driver who found me abandoned on his front seat drove for the Larkin Clothing Company." Jayne's voice was so quiet that he had to lean closer to hear her words. "With the boys it didn't seem to matter so much, but when I had my little girl, I suddenly wanted to be able to hand something down to her. The name was all I had." She looked up at Alex and smiled. "Sounds ridiculous now, doesn't it?"

"Not at all." Alex took a deep breath and told her about his middle name and how he "borrowed" it from Richard Chamberlain during his Dr. Kildare days. Jayne was the first person he'd ever told. "The need for a family history is stronger than people think."

"Is that a professional opinion?"

"Strictly personal."

"I knew we were kindred spirits." She squeezed his hand and Alex wondered how life would have been if he'd had a mother like Jayne Walker.

"Your daughter is very lucky, Jayne."

"I don't think she would have agreed with you when she was growing up, Alex." Obviously, Jayne sensed his mood and tried to lighten the atmosphere in the kitchen. She described the lengths to which Larkin would go to avoid housework chores. "One time she took her bicycle and we found her halfway to Hoover Dam. Looking back, I think I should have gone easier on her, but I didn't know how to do anything for myself when I married, and I didn't want my daughter to have to learn to cook from her husband."

"Bill taught you to cook?" To hear Larkin talk, her mother had been born with a spoon in one hand and a saucepan in the other.

"Bill taught me to cook, clean and run a household. I was twenty-two, and all I could do was make scrambled eggs and do a high kick you wouldn't believe."

"The way Larkin described Bill, I thought he was a man of the old school."

"Larkin and her father have been at odds since the day she was born. She's just as independent and stubborn as he is and, deep down, they're crazy about each other. Bill is prouder of her success than the success of any of the boys." Bill Walker had actually guided Larkin through the financial maze of business loans when she started the Learning Center.

Some of the puzzle pieces began to fit together for Alex.

"Unfortunately, my daughter has the opinion I'm under my husband's thumb," Jayne continued. "The truth is that I make my own decisions—I always have. It's simply that I know how priceless a family is, and I've chosen to spend my life nurturing a beautiful one."

"A fine choice," Alex said. "One I would like to make myself."

"Give her time," Jayne said with another pat on his hand. "I'm afraid Larkin led a charmed life—she never knew what it was like to want something and be unable to have it until Vladimir—" Jayne stopped abruptly. "You don't want me to be indiscreet, do you?"

"Of course I do." He wanted to know everything he possibly could about the woman he loved and the man who preceded him.

Jayne laughed. "I can't."

"I realize that."

"It will work out, Alex. You'll see."

"Am I that transparent?"

"Only to a kindred spirit."

Jayne met his eyes, and he saw warmth and understanding and a love so all-encompassing that he felt it would be a privilege to be part of the family she had created.

For two weeks he'd been doing his damnedest not to pressure Larkin into making a commitment. For two weeks he'd also been doing his damnedest to keep from whisking her away to Las Vegas in his Cessna and marrying her before she had a chance to think straight.

Maybe it was time to stop thinking and time to start acting.

THE SCENE at Larkin's dinner table was as perfect a picture of familial happiness as Larkin had ever encountered. Norman Rockwell might have looked askance at the assortment of individuals who gave thanks for the year's bounty, but to Larkin it was magazine-cover perfect.

Bill had abandoned the TV set and had settled his rangy body in a chair close enough to the den that he could still hear the game play by play. Jayne, beaming with pleasure, sat next to him. Gordon had come with Patti, fully prepared to repair the loose bricks in Larkin's fireplace. She had laughed and told him that he was there as a guest, but apparently he became uncomfortable, because he left soon after. Patti stayed on, flamboyant as usual in a bright purple jump suit with yellow earrings the size of squash blossoms.

Roger amused everyone with stories about growing up playing piano in a family of transit workers and bricklayers, and his friend Kurt's pungent asides even made straitlaced Bill laugh out loud.

And then there was Alex.

He sat at the opposite end of her pine trestle table and it seemed to Larkin as if he had always been at the center of her life. The fact that her parents liked him, too, made her reluctance to make a commitment seem incomprehensible even to her. Alex was as different from Vladimir Karpov as today's Larkin was from the Larkin who had fallen gracelessly in love with the dancer.

Just one more week, she whispered silently, watching Alex's face as he talked to her father. One more week and the ballet workshop would be over and Vladimir would be out of her life—and her mind—for good.

Just one more week and she'd be able to tell Alex all that was in her heart.

"Larkin!"

Patti's voice brought her back to the dinner table.

"If we're going to put on our tap-dance extravaganza, we'd better get dessert started. Your mom and dad have to leave soon for the airport."

Larkin leaped up. "I'll start the coffee."

Alex, at the far end of the table, stood up as well. "I'll help."

The dinner dishes had already been cleared, and it was obvious that plugging in a coffee maker did not require the services of two healthy adults. Larkin saw a few sly glances cast in their direction, but she pretended not to notice.

She was in Alex's arms before the kitchen door closed behind him.

"The old start-the-coffee trick," Alex said as he dipped her over his arm in a very theatrical embrace. "I like your style."

"I don't think anyone out there believed it for a minute," she said, breathless from his kiss.

He leaned against the worktable and pulled her close against him. "They probably know we're in here making out like teenagers."

Indeed, she felt like a teenager, giddy with excitement and pleasure. He lightly stroked her breast through the covering of the same red silk dress she'd been wearing the day they met. "We should be ashamed of ourselves—my parents are right in the other room."

He moved against her in a frankly sexual manner and she wasn't ashamed of herself at all—she wanted to flaunt her love in front of everyone, to shout from the rooftops that what she felt for Alex was the real thing.

Of course, her kitchen on Thanksgiving Day with family and friends in the next room was hardly the place to get seriously intimate. Alex nipped at her neck, and she giggled and moved away.

"Maybe we should start the coffee," she said.

"Maybe we should sneak away for a while."

"They want dessert."

"So do I."

"Behave yourself." She switched on the coffee maker on the counter. "I'd hate to be caught flagrante delicto."

"It would make a Thanksgiving they'd never forget."

"I'd rather they remember my pumpkin pie, not my—"

The front doorbell chimed. She looked at Alex. "Do you think Phil and Judy made it after all?"

Alex glanced at his watch. "I doubt it. With traffic, they never could have made it out from Brooklyn this early. Besides, didn't they say they'd call?"

"I suppose we should go out and see who it is."

"I suppose so." He pulled her back into his arms.

"I could stay here forever."

"Why don't you?"

She raised her head toward his and just as his mouth was about to meet hers, Patti's unmistakable voice blasted both of them out of their romantic mood.

"Laaarkin! Come here!"

"The natives are getting restless," Alex muttered as Larkin opened the kitchen door. "Talk about caffeine dependency."

Larkin was still chuckling over his comment when they entered the dining room. Her smile froze.

There—bigger, blonder and even more magnificent than she'd remembered—stood Vladimir Karpov, all six feet four inches of him swathed in a full-length fur coat that seriously endangered at least three species.

"Well, my love, have you nothing to say to me after so long?" He started toward her.

Before she knew what was happening she was swept up into his arms and enveloped in an embrace that buried her face in the soft fur of his coat. She was acutely aware of the silence in the room and of the tension building inside Alex.

She recovered her equilibrium and her voice simultaneously. "What brings you here?"

"Not the most gracious of greetings," he said, flashing the room one of his neon smiles, "but it will do for now." He motioned toward the driveway. "The car picked me up at the airport, and we were on the—how do you put it?—Expressway and I see your town and say, 'On an American holiday, where else will I find my little bourgeois darling but home?'"

God help her, but her knees were beginning to give way. Just seeing Vladimir catapulted her back in time to when a smile from him meant the world. Old habits, it seemed, were hard to break.

She took a deep breath. "Well, your bourgeois darling is home with her family, Vladimir, enjoying a private family holiday. You should have called."

His smile widened, and she swore she heard a gasp of admiration from Patti's vicinity. "I wish I had, my love. Perhaps then I could have enjoyed your feast."

Damn it! How did he manage to make the simplest sentence sound so erotic? "As it is, you're too late." She glanced over at Alex, but his eyes were riveted on Vladimir. He wasn't alone. Everyone's eyes were riveted on Vladimir.

She cleared her throat and was about to introduce Vladimir to everyone when he noticed Jayne and Bill and swooped them into a furry bear hug.

"How long!" His voice boomed. "How long since I've seen you!"

Bill extricated himself from the embrace, spitting out bits of fur coat. Jayne, however, smiled up at the Russian, and only Larkin could see the reserve on her lovely face.

Larkin turned to Alex, who stood perfectly still in the doorway to the dining room, arms folded across his chest. "I'm sorry," she said quietly. "I wasn't expecting him here."

"That's Karpov, isn't it?"

She nodded miserably, watching Vladimir weave his spell around Roger and Kurt and a most willing Patti. "Afraid so. He's never been one to stand on ceremony."

Alex eyed Karpov's fur coat. "Or good taste, either."

"He's flamboyant. A lot of dancers are like that."

Suddenly Vladimir was in front of them, with Patti just a few steps behind. She looked positively bedazzled, and it wasn't difficult at all for Larkin to remember a time when she had felt the same way about him.

The two men stood eye to eye, and Larkin wished she were anyplace but there in her dining room. Siberia didn't sound bad—it couldn't be half as cold as the looks they were giving one another.

Vladimir smiled slightly, and she could see that he was trying to figure out exactly where Alex entered into this family scene. She knew she should put her arm around Alex or take his hand or do something that would make their relationship clear, but she felt paralyzed on the spot, unable to think, much less react.

"Vladimir, this is Dr. Alex Jakobs."

Alex extended his hand and Vladimir shook it.

"Doctor of medicine?"

"Doctor of psychology."

"I have heard of you somewhere?" Larkin flinched at Vladimir's words.

Alex, however, kept his cool. "Probably not."

She cleared her throat, aware of everyone's eyes upon her. "Alex has a very successful television show on cable, Vladimir. He's quite well known."

Vladimir looked directly at Alex. "I should be watching over my shoulder for you, your popularity is so great with Larkin?"

"I can't speak for my popularity with Larkin, but I would definitely watch over my shoulder, if I were you."

Vladimir threw his head back and laughed, that big, booming laugh Larkin once loved so well. Now it seemed to overpower the small dining room. He looked down at Larkin, and she wished she could disappear behind the credenza and not come out until Christmas.

"This man is too smart for me," he said in his heavily accented voice. "Dancers—we say things much better with our bodies." He put an arm around Larkin's shoulders. "Some things can be expressed only with the art of movement."

Jayne moved a step closer to Alex. "I disagree," she said. "Alex works with words. That, too, is an art."

The look Alex gave her mother made Larkin realize just how badly she was handling the situation. She'd been taken by surprise—that was it. She'd been prepared to meet Vladimir again at the Center, surrounded by visible proof of her success. Traces of the naive young woman he'd known would be hidden safely behind expensive clothing and a veneer of sophistication only recently acquired. She moved out of his embrace.

Vladimir had no business standing there in her home on a family holiday making her feel as gauche and awkward as he had when they were lovers. He had no business turning a lighthearted occasion into something fraught with more undercurrents than a river in flood.

And she had no business allowing it all to happen.

"Speaking of movement," she said, her non sequitur giving everyone a second's pause, "Mom and Patti and I were about to provide some after-dinner entertainment. Would you care to stay?" Polite. Casual. Boring. Certainly he would refuse.

"How can I refuse such an offer? Did I not say movement of all kind is my passion?"

"I don't recall specifying what kind of entertainment we were offering, Vladimir."

"Is not necessary, my love. I know you too well. Dance was once as important as I was to you."

She glanced at Alex, but his face remained impassive. *Say something,* she told herself. *Make it obvious you're in love with Alex. Don't let this idiotic situation go on any longer.*

"Come on," Patti urged, her color unnaturally high as she stood next to Vladimir. "Let's give them that show we promised!"

Vladimir looked from Alex to Larkin then draped his arm across Patti's shoulders. Patti looked as if she'd won the New York State lottery, and Larkin's stomach knotted. She'd been in Patti's position, and she knew the jolt of pure elation Vladimir's attentions could generate. And even though she knew the flip side of that elation, for a split second she envied Patti the sensation of standing in the eye of the storm.

She looked up at Alex. His handsome face was as closed to her as a locked door. "What should I do?" she asked softly.

"Whatever you want to do."

"I don't know what I want to do."

"And that's the problem, isn't it?" For a second the shield dropped, and she saw the pain she'd caused him and her heart twisted.

"Come on," Patti urged, grabbing Larkin and propelling her toward the doorway. "Let's get into costume." She executed a clumsy high kick. "Remember, the show must go on!"

Larkin looked from Alex to Vladimir and back again. The collision between past and present had her reeling.

It was hard for the show to go on when your future was crumbling all around your tap-dancing feet.

Chapter Seventeen

Alex wasn't prone to violence by nature, but from the first moment Karpov burst into the house in that ridiculous fur coat of his, Alex had been fighting down the urge to deck him. He liked to think he was a reasonable man, well beyond such primitive outbursts, but every time he looked at Larkin and saw the vulnerable look in her eyes, he wanted his fist to connect with Karpov's face.

An irrational wish, maybe. But very, very appealing.

It hadn't escaped Alex's notice that Bill Walker didn't seem thrilled to see Karpov again. Bill grunted a hello then went back to discussing football with Roger and Kurt—an unlikely alliance, if ever there was one. Even Jayne, the kindest woman he'd ever met, had difficulty bridging the gap between the social niceties and her real feelings about the Russian. Patti was practically swooning at Karpov's suede-booted feet, but Alex knew she was a sucker for a handsome face.

All of their reactions made sense to Alex; Larkin's, however, did not. Where he had expected her to be flustered, she was cool. Where he had expected anger, she was excruciatingly polite. Where he had expected her to cling to his side, making their relationship obvious to Karpov, she made a point of standing alone.

And it hurt.

He'd been so busy being jealous over Larkin's past that it hadn't occurred to him that it was really her future—*their* future together—that he had to worry about.

Looking over at Karpov, who was reclining in a lounge chair by the fire watching Larkin with eyes that hid a thousand memories, Alex understood for the first time that he just might lose her.

GOD KNOWS THEY TRIED hard, but the show was a disaster. Jayne was terrific, but Larkin lacked enthusiasm, and Patti was so busy staring at Vladimir that twice she forgot what she was doing and stumbled over the ribbon laces on her tap shoes. Larkin was glad when Alex looked at his watch and said they'd better leave for the airport in twenty minutes or Bill and Jayne would miss their flight to London. The dinner party broke up.

She followed Roger and Kurt toward the hall closet where the coats were stashed. "Please stay," she urged. "Alex can take my parents to the airport and—"

"I'm a working man," Roger said. "Where would Rick's Place be without their peripatetic piano player? Besides, I'm not going to run interference for you." He gave a theatrical shiver. "Too dangerous in there for me."

Kurt said good-night and slipped unobtrusively out onto the porch.

"I don't need you to run interference, Roger. I'd just like you to stay. We've been having such a great time."

"We have? That's news to me."

"Our performance wasn't very good, was it?"

"It stunk."

"You could try to be a bit more diplomatic, Lacey."

"Sometimes it's kinder to be cruel. I don't think Dr. J. was having the time of his life, either."

"He loves tap dancing, even bad tap dancing."

"The tap dancing wasn't his problem. It was the audience."

So Roger had noticed the tension in the room as well. "There's nothing between Vladimir and me any longer. Alex knows that."

"You don't sound too sure, darling."

"Of course I'm sure." She tried to keep her voice at a normal pitch. "You saw the way Vladimir was looking at Patti in there."

"Everyone looked at Patti. It's hard to ignore a woman who falls into the fireplace."

"I don't like you when you're difficult, Lacey."

"And I don't like you when you're dishonest, Walker." He put his arm around her. "You're not still in love with that bozo, are you?"

"God forbid! I'm not a masochist, Roger. Once was more than enough."

"Glad to hear it, because he made a play for Patti while you were digging up the dance music."

She was silent for a moment, trying to ignore an irrational twinge of jealousy. "I hope she understands what she's up against," she said finally. "Vladimir is the big time when it comes to heartbreak."

Roger squeezed her shoulder. "Our Miss Franklin knows the rules of the game."

"There are no rules to the game, Roger. Didn't anybody ever tell you that?"

"You sound cynical."

"I was aiming for sophistication."

"I miss these talks," Roger said. "Now that you and Dr. J. are a hot item, there doesn't seem to be as much time."

She ruffled his short blond hair. Roger seemed happier, more at ease, than ever before. "I miss you, too."

"Ain't love grand?" Roger hugged her and slipped into his jacket. "Just hang on to the good doctor. Don't go getting dazzled by a little glitz and glamour."

"I'm not in any danger," she said. "Things between us are long over."

Roger, however, didn't seem convinced. "It ain't over till it's over, kid."

"Did you get that from a fortune cookie?"

"No. Yogi Berra, chapter three, verse eighteen."

With those words of wisdom from an unlikely philosopher, Roger took his leave.

Larkin went back into the dining room. Her parents were upstairs getting ready to depart, and Alex had disappeared out the side door to load the Walkers' suitcases into the trunk of his car. Patti was in the den changing out of her dance costume and, unfortunately, only Vladimir remained.

He was still magnificent to look at. Age had done nothing to diminish the force of his blond-and-bronzed splendor. He was seated on one of her straight-back dining room chairs, his long legs extended in front of him and his arms casually crossed over his chest. He made jeans and a black sweater look like a full-page ad in *Gentleman's Quarterly*.

"I have to change," Larkin said, standing in the doorway in her spangled leotard. "If you'd like coffee, there's some in the kitchen."

Vladimir unfolded his long, lean body and stood, taking up much more space than he had any right to. Stage presence like his had no place in her bourgeois dining room on Thanksgiving Day. He was next to her before she could draw another breath, blocking her view of the rest of the room.

"I do not like your new friend."

"I know Roger will be devastated to hear that."

"I do not talk about Roger."

"Somehow I didn't think so." She moved slightly away from him until she felt the dining room wall against her back. "Alex?"

Vladimir nodded. His shimmering blond hair fell across his forehead, and he tossed it back with a gesture that evoked other places, other times. "This is the Alex from your trip to Virginia, yes?"

"Yes."

"He is your lover?"

"That's none of your business." *Not anymore.*

"I care about you, Larkin."

"Then you should be pleased that I'm happy."

"This Alex is not the right one for you, my love. He is not the sort of man I picture you with."

Who would have figured Vladimir Karpov to play the spurned lover three years after she walked out the door? "Any specific complaints?" she asked lightly. "Alex seems perfect to me."

Vladimir trailed his right hand down the length of her silky hair, and for a split second she felt the heat from his fire.

"But not perfect for you, my love. This Alex is ruled by his intellect. You need a man ruled by passion."

"I need a man ruled by his heart." *Tell him you love Alex. Tell him. Put an end to this before it goes any farther.* The words, however, would not come, and she hated herself for it. She'd waited a long time to have Vladimir understand what he lost when she left him, and she wanted to enjoy the victory—however small.

Vladimir, supremely confident even in the most trying circumstances, smiled at her. "We have time," he said. "I can amuse myself for tonight, but tomorrow you come to me at my hotel, and we talk about the old and the new. I still remember the feel of you in my arms—even after so long."

Damn him to hell. He always knew how to shift the balance in his favor. Before Larkin could frame an answer, Patti, radiant with anticipation, floated into the room.

"I'm ready," Patti said, touching his forearm the way an artist would touch the *Pietà.* She turned to Larkin. "Vladimir is taking me to that new club on the Lower East Side."

He bent down and nuzzled the small redhead behind the ear. "She is a treasure, is she not? I like to exhibit my treasures for all to envy."

Cynical, wisecracking Patti Franklin, who believed Adam's first words to Eve were a lie, bought it all—hook, line and sinker.

Vladimir met Larkin's eyes over Patti's head, and the look of sexual promise in his eyes sizzled through her body. The temptation was there, hot and promising and more dangerous than ever. *It ain't over till it's over.* Roger's bit of baseball philosophy didn't seem quite so funny any longer.

Old loves altered, old loves faded but old loves rarely died. Not for Alex and apparently not for her. Suddenly the future didn't seem quite so clear as it had before Vladimir showed up at her doorstep.

She wondered what Yogi Berra would say about that.

HE WAITED AN HOUR until he was certain they were at the airport before he came out of the shadows alongside her house.

He was in luck. Obviously, the shrink had forgotten to double-lock her side door, and jimmying the tumbler was a simple task. He was inside her house within moments.

The kitchen gleamed. Only the faint aroma of turkey and pumpkin pie lingered to give away the fact that a feast had been prepared in that room. He would have liked to have stayed long enough that afternoon to enjoy the food, the sight of her across the table, but the visions that lingered behind his eyes had made it impossible for him to sit still while the bearded man claimed her in front of everyone.

But a promise was a promise. He said he would repair the loose bricks in the fireplace, and repair them he would. He headed through the hallway to the den on the other side of the house, but stopped at the door to her bedroom, suddenly overpowered by the need to have something of hers—to be close to things she touched.

He slid open the top drawer of her dresser and let the silky things drift through his fingers. The scent of her perfume filled his nostrils, and he wondered how much longer he would be able to go on without her.

Fantasies once were enough.

They weren't any longer.

"LAST CALL FOR passengers boarding Flight 536 to London at Gate 11."

They just made it in time. Alex, who had been thoroughly enjoying the company of Bill and Jayne Walker, was almost disappointed. "I think they mean business this time, folks."

Larkin handed Bill her mother's carry-on luggage. "Alex is right. Unless you guys want to end up crossing the Atlantic in a one-engine Cessna, we'd better get you to the gate."

"I wouldn't mind taking a trip in that Cessna one day," Bill said, shaking Alex's hand. "I'm going to hold you to that offer of a ride, Alex, and soon."

Bill's handshake was as direct and strong as the man himself. "It's a deal," Alex said. "When you come back from London, I'll take both of you up for a ride."

Jayne shivered. "Larkin showed me the pictures of that plane of yours. I'll have to sign up for one of her 'fear of flying' courses before we go up."

Larkin and Bill stepped aside to talk business for a moment and Alex hugged Jayne.

"There's nothing to it," he said. "You'll love it."

"A likely story," Jayne said, hugging him back. "That's what they said about the *Titanic.*"

"Don't worry. I promise we won't hit any icebergs, Jayne."

"Not like the one we hit this evening?"

For a second he thought he'd missed something. Icebergs on a warmish evening in late November? Then he understood. "You're talking about our unexpected visitor?"

"He had no business popping in like that. Larkin should have shown him the door."

Alex had thought the same thing at the time, but chalked it up to male jealousy. Interesting that Larkin's mother would share his feelings. He wondered if Jayne had noticed the abrupt change in Larkin as soon as Karpov appeared.

"You taught your daughter well, Jayne. She's much too polite to toss someone out on his ear."

Jayne patted his arm. "Don't let him get to you."

"I'm doing my best."

"My daughter is no fool. She knows a good man when she finds one."

He grinned, looking over at Bill and Larkin. "Takes after her mother, does she?"

"When it comes to the important things in life." Jayne kissed Alex's cheek, and he had to force down emotions so intense that tears burned behind his eyelids. "She's been hurt, Alex, and she's afraid of being hurt again. She'll come around."

Jayne's words lingered with him as he and Larkin left the airport after seeing them off. The car windows were rolled down, and the damp, salty air washed over them as he drove along the almost deserted Southern State Parkway toward her house. It was unseasonably warm, and Larkin was uncharacteristically quiet—the combination made him jittery and unsure of himself, and twice he had to force his attention back to his driving.

"Is something wrong?" Larkin asked as he exited onto the Robert Moses Parkway and headed south. "Do we need gas?"

"It's a nice night. I thought we might go out to the beach."

She nodded but said nothing. Since they left the airport, he and Larkin had talked about Jayne's dancing, Bill's football mania, Roger's relationship and Gordon's abrupt disappearance before dinner, but not one word had been said about Vladimir Karpov. Alex could sense Larkin distancing herself from him, and the thought that he just might be losing her scared hell out of him.

Tonight's interlude with Vladimir was only a coming attraction. The Russian was going to be in town, actively involved with the Center for the next five days, and although the workshop would run perfectly without constant supervision, Alex knew that Larkin would be on hand to orchestrate every movement. A week ago that hadn't bothered him.

Tonight it made him crazy.

He was tired of playing it safe, tired of holding back, tired of not saying exactly what was on his mind. Logic stood him in good stead in his career, but it had no place in matters of the heart.

He loved Larkin and wanted to spend the rest of his life with her, and it was high time he told her.

He turned off onto the unlighted access road. The beach was officially closed for the winter; the guardhouse windows stared blankly toward the road. He parked his car at the western edge of the lot on a rise that overlooked the water, then turned off the engine. The silence was all-encompassing, and he wondered if she could hear the pounding of his heart.

ON ANOTHER NIGHT, in another mood, the beach would have been magical.

Stars twinkled off the ocean, and it was difficult to tell where the midnight water ended and the night sky began. A nearly full moon, silvery-pale, hung low in the sky. Larkin wished she could snap her fingers and force herself out of her melancholy mood, but at the moment magic was beyond her reach.

It had disappeared the second Vladimir showed up at her house.

Her home was her source of strength, and she shared it only with the people she cared most about. He had no business showing up there with his obscene fur coat and silver-screen smile, making her feel as awkward and clumsy as she had during her time with him.

Now when she saw him again at the reception on Saturday, he would know that beneath the sophisticated surface of Larkin Walker, entrepreneur, beat the same soft heart of the Larkin Walker who had once loved him a long time ago.

In the hands of someone like Vladimir, that was dangerous information indeed. Maybe turning the whole thing over to Patti and the staff wasn't a bad idea at that. There was something to be said for a dignified retreat.

Alex turned off the engine. "Are you up to a stroll on the beach?"

"I'm too lazy to move," she said, curling up on the plush front seat. "Post-turkey fatigue."

He reached over and stroked her hair. "Want to just sit here and enjoy the view?"

She nodded. "If you don't mind. I've never been much of an outdoors type. Besides, it's deserted out there. This feels a lot safer."

He looked at her for a moment, but let her last comment slide, much to her relief. She was feeling emotionally vulnerable, and any professional probing—no matter how well-intentioned—would expose raw nerve.

She changed the subject. "I hope you know my dad will never let you rest until you take him up in your Cessna. That promise will haunt you, Alex."

"I'll take both of them up as soon as they get back from London. The four of us could fly up to New Hampshire for a little skiing."

"I don't ski," Larkin said. "Bad knees, remember?"

He glanced down at her legs. "They don't look that bad to me."

"Don't let appearances deceive you, Dr. Jakobs. Inside, they're a mess."

He pushed the armrest up and moved closer to her. She caught the faint scent of peppermint from a chocolate mint Jayne had given him back at the airport.

"There are other things we could do on a snowy weekend," he said. "We could send your parents out on the slopes and we could stay behind, enjoying a little après-ski diversion."

"I'm afraid skiing is a prerequisite for après-ski, Alex. Otherwise, it's just called loafing around."

He put his arm around her and kissed the side of her throat. "There's one other thing we could do."

There was something about the tone of his voice that made her breath catch. "Sightsee?"

He turned her face toward his. His eyes seemed silver in the moonlight, and she knew before he even said the words. "We could get married, Larkin."

"I don't think it's a prerequisite for a ski weekend, Alex," she said, a clumsy attempt at a joke.

"I'm not joking, Larkin. We could fly up to Newport. There's a little inn there that—"

"Oh, Alex. I don't know what to say."

"You could say, 'I love you,' for starters."

She touched his cheek. "I *do* love you. Surely you must know that by now."

"But?"

How well he knew her. "But I need more time. This is happening so quickly. We've known each other only seven weeks."

"Seven days or seven lifetimes—it doesn't matter if it's right."

She waited too long to respond. For the rest of her life she'd remember the look of pain on his handsome face.

"But it's not right, is it, Larkin? Not tonight."

"I don't know what you mean." She prayed his logic would fail him just this once.

"Karpov," he said. "You're still in love with him, aren't you?"

"I love you, Alex. Vladimir is in my past."

"You don't sound certain."

There was no way she could explain to Alex the battle she'd fought to regain her self-esteem. She was not proud of the woman she used to be and not willing to expose her weaknesses before the man she loved. She owed him no explanations. None at all. "I have nothing to prove to you, Alex. If you don't believe me, that's your problem."

"The problem is yours, Larkin." His voice was rough, raw with emotion. It was a fiery, almost out-of-control Alex Jakobs she'd never before seen. "You can't let go of your past, but you're too damned scared to grab hold of your future."

"I wouldn't pursue that topic any further, Alex."

"What does that mean?"

"Are you certain you're over Rikki?"

"Rikki's dead," he snapped.

"And if she weren't?" *Insane question.* She was about to get the answer she deserved.

"We'd still be married."

"Thanks for the honest answer. It goes well with a proposal of marriage."

"How about I withdraw the proposal of marriage?" The look in his eyes was as dark and dangerous as the ocean a few hundred feet away. "Obviously, it was not one of my better ideas."

"Do whatever you like," she said, surprised a heart could stand so much pain and not stop beating. "I really don't give a damn anymore."

"Karpov will be happy to hear that. Maybe when he's done with Patti, he can work you into his schedule."

She raised her hand. "I've never slapped a man in my life," she said quietly, "but I wish to God I had the guts to make an exception."

He tried neither to stop her nor move out of her reach. As much as she wanted to strike out at him physically, she was unable to follow through. Alex, at least, had been honest—something she was unable to manage at the moment. Her hand fell down to her lap. She clenched her fist to hide the tremor.

"Smart move," he said. "I can't vouch for my self-control at the moment."

The air between them crackled.

"I'd like to go home," she said, staring straight ahead into the darkness.

"A perfect ending to a romantic night," he said, starting the engine. "You and Karpov can tell your grandchildren about this one."

"I had no idea you were prone to melodrama, Alex. It doesn't become you."

"Neither does being made a fool of, Larkin. If you'd leveled with me weeks ago, I could still have enjoyed the pleasure and avoided the pain."

She looked at him blankly.

"You're not that naive," he said, backing out of the parking space. "Sex and love don't always march hand in hand, Larkin. Certainly Karpov taught you that much, didn't he?"

This time the pain was more than she could bear, and before she could think, her hand connected with the taut skin of his left cheek. Instead of satisfaction, she felt shame. The sound of the slap echoed in her ears. Her palm tingled from the contact. She wished he would strike back, tell her to go to hell, do something.

Instead, he watched the road. The only evidence of her action was the way a small vein throbbed at the base of his throat and the terrible, vibrating sensation of finality that filled the car as they headed back toward the parkway.

THE SOUND OF A CAR in front of her house snapped him abruptly out of his reverie. Careful to stay out of the light, he crouched by the window, a silky peach slip clutched in his hand, and listened.

A car door opened and shut. He waited, expecting to hear the sound of footsteps rounding the car and another door opening and closing.

Her high heels tapped against the flagstone path, and he held his breath as he heard the sound of her key in the lock.

The house was silent and dark, and they were all alone.

The time had finally come.

Chapter Eighteen

Alex waited at the curb, car engine racing, until she had her front door open; before she could turn around, he threw the car in gear and was gone.

The house, which had been filled with laughter just a few hours earlier, seemed cavernous and silent. All of the words Larkin had longed to say to Alex to repair the damage between them still echoed in her brain, trapped behind pride and anger.

A bone-weary fatigue swept over her as she switched on the kitchen light and turned the gas on under the kettle. Her plans to settle down with a pot of tea and try to make some sense out of the day vanished before her exhaustion. The tea still sounded fine, but now all she wanted to do was crawl beneath the covers and not think at all.

The first order of business was to get out of her festive holiday dress and into her robe. She was padding through the hallway toward her room when she heard a scratching sound from the den.

"Amanda?" Larkin hadn't noticed the elderly cat in the living room. "No nocturnal rambles tonight, please, Amanda. Have mercy."

She doubled back toward the den, mumbling about feline eccentricities. Her dress was unzipped and she had already shed her shoes and panty hose. The thought of getting dressed again was more than she could bear. She turned on the light to the den.

"Amanda! How many times have I—"

She stopped cold. There, standing by the fireplace, was Gordon Franklin.

IT WASN'T UNTIL a cop pulled Alex over on Jericho Turnpike and gave him a warning for reckless driving that he realized what he was doing. It was one thing to have a death wish yourself, but it was quite another thing entirely to take anyone else along with you.

He pulled into a diner and went inside for a cup of coffee. He hadn't been drinking, but obviously he needed a chance to get on top of things again.

"Tough night?" the waitress asked as she plunked down a menu and clean silverware.

"The toughest."

"Family fight?"

He nodded. Close enough.

"It's the holidays," the waitress said, yanking her order pad from her uniform pocket. "Makes everybody crazy. If people just stayed home and worked things out, we'd be a lot better off." She smiled at him. "Of course, then I'd be outta business. What can I get you?"

He ordered coffee and a ham on rye, and she hurried off. The diner was surprisingly crowded, but it did little to ease the loneliness that had been building since he left Larkin at her house. He had watched her slender figure hurry along the flagstone path, praying that she would turn around and come back into his arms. Instead, she took her keys out of her pocket, opened the door and disappeared inside without glancing back at him once.

The waitress brought the coffee. It was dark, hot and lousy. It suited him perfectly.

"You damned fool," he muttered.

The waitress glared at him. "Hold your horses, mister. Your ham on rye's on the way."

He stood up and fished a five-dollar bill out of his pocket. "Keep the change," he said, handing it to her as he headed for the door. "And thanks for the advice."

"I don't give no advice," she called after him. "I just make observations."

And damned good ones, he thought as he started his car. For all of his years of training, for all of his experience working with men and women in transition, he had been unable to recognize the fact that Larkin had been hurt as he had.

Rikki's death had come close to devastating him, but he'd been able to return to the land of the living and take comfort in the memories of their life together. Larkin's memories of her time with Karpov offered little in the way of comfort. Larkin might have been the one to walk out, but she'd left much of her self-esteem behind. The clues had been there all the time, and if he hadn't been so blinded with love and jealousy, he would have realized it a long time ago.

He headed toward the highway. Loving someone meant opening your heart to pain, but loving someone was the single best reason for man's existence that anyone had yet come up with.

In fifteen minutes he'd be at her house, and even if he had to sit on her doorstep all night, he would do his damnedest to hold on to what they had. Any man lucky enough to find love twice in his life would be a fool to let it slip away without a fight.

And, if nothing else, Alex Jakobs was a fighter.

SHE LEANED AGAINST the doorway. Her heart pounded violently against her ribs. "Gordon!"

"Sorry to scare you, Larkin," Gordon said, looking up. "I didn't hear you come in."

"How did you get in here?"

He smiled at her, fiddling around with some tools scattered in front of the fireplace. "Dr. Jakobs left the side door open. Better tell him to be more careful. Someone could get in here."

Someone obviously already did. Her heart still thudded against her ribs and she took a deep breath to calm down.

"What are you doing here, Gordon?"

"You asked me to fix the fireplace, didn't you?"

"Fix it, yes," she said, "but it didn't have to be tonight."

"Winter's coming. You might need it."

"In case you haven't noticed, it's sixty-two degrees out there tonight, Gordon. We're hardly in danger of a sudden frost."

"It's almost December," he persisted. "Besides, I wanted to surprise you."

He took a step closer to her. Why hadn't she noticed how tall he was, how strong? She'd been so conscious of him as Patti Franklin's little brother that she'd never had a strong physical awareness of him as a man before that very moment.

He smiled at her, and she backed away. Was that the look Alex had noticed weeks ago? How on earth could she have missed it?

"Well, you succeeded," she said. "You surprised me." *Be calm. Everything's fine. It's only Gordon.* "Let's worry about the fireplace another time. I'm tired and . . ." She let her words trail off, offering him the opportunity to make a graceful, face-saving exit.

He continued toward her. "I thought you would be happy I was here," he said, trailing his hand along her cheek. "You are happy, aren't you? I want you to be happy."

The shy boy she had known was turning, before her eyes, into a caricature of himself. The touch of his hand against her skin caused bile to rise into her throat.

He touched her hair, and she jerked away. Her reflexive action seemed to anger him.

"I've watched you for so long," he said. "You've made me wait for so long."

What in hell was he talking about? He had never been more than Patti's brother to her, a young guy life hadn't been very kind to. She'd known he had some emotional problems, but she hadn't figured on anything like this.

His arm went around her body; his fingers pressed against her waist in a possessive way. A scream echoed in her brain, and she wondered if she could possibly break away from him and reach the phone. A great idea if it worked but potentially dangerous if it didn't. This Gordon was not the malleable young man who worked at the Center.

This Gordon was a man in a state of heat.

She thought of Alex and the way he talked his way around Karen O'Rourke's attempted suicide that long-ago night at the TV studio.

"Don't do this, Gordon," she said, forcing her voice to stay neutral. "Don't do something you'll be embarrassed over later." He was so close that she could smell faint traces of liquor on his breath. "If you leave right now, we can forget the whole thing."

He hesitated; his grip on her waist loosened slightly. "I can't forget," he said, his body pushing against hers. "I want to touch you. I've wanted to for so long."

Good God. He was pressing against her, hard and demanding, and terror rocketed through her body. From the back pocket of his jeans he removed one of her pale-peach slips, and the look on his face as he slid the silky fabric across her face would stay with her forever.

"Let me go, Gordon," she said, struggling against him. "You can't do this. I won't let you do this."

He cupped her breasts. "You like it when he does it," he said in her ear. "You'll like it when I do it even more. I love you."

"But I don't love you." She brought her fist hard against his lower abdomen. "You have no right to touch me." Her punch had no effect on him at all.

"This gives me the right." He rubbed against her and his erection burned against her thigh.

The fabric of her dress tore easily. He was stronger than she, and all of the rational talk in the world wasn't about to stop him from taking what he wanted.

INSTEAD OF PULLING into the driveway as he normally would, Alex parked his car on the street. He didn't want to signal his arrival and give Larkin time to think about all the reasons why she might not want to talk with him.

He followed the flagstone path to her front door and was about to ring the bell when he noticed a silhouette in the den.

Curious, he stepped back for a better look. His gut wrenched as if he'd taken a punch. There, outlined against the shade, was Larkin—her slim curves unmistakable—in the arms of a tall and muscular man. He backed away, unable to tear his eyes from the intimate shape their forms made, and tripped over a loose flagstone.

You stupid son-of-a-bitch. He slammed his hand against the trunk of an oak tree alongside the house. *You damn fool.* He'd seen the way Karpov looked at Larkin. He'd felt the pull between them, even if he'd been unable to understand it. Why should he be surprised that she fell back into the Russian's arms?

In a flash Alex was back in his car. The engine leaped to life immediately and he was about to tear away from there when logic—the one constant in his life—reappeared.

You know her better than that, Jakobs. She wouldn't turn to Karpov like this. Not tonight. The Larkin he knew would rant and rave and ultimately take to bed with Amanda and a good book, not an old lover.

Sweat broke out on his forehead and slithered down his temples. There was one more possibility—one that he had almost forgotten.

The phone calls, the damaged car, the necklace Larkin received, the dead birds on his doorstep with the gold chain around their necks—the look on Gordon Franklin's face each time he saw Alex.

Suddenly it all made sense. He flung himself from the car and tore up the driveway to the front door. Gordon was obsessed with Larkin and, if Alex's Ph.D. was worth anything at all, he could be sure the next step was destruction of the object of the obsession.

Larkin.

The front door was double-locked. He ran around back to the flimsy kitchen door and kicked it open. The shrill scream of the teakettle sent chills up his spine as he ran for the den. He prayed he wasn't too late.

LARKIN'S HEART POUNDED. *Think of something. For God's sake, think of something.*

Gordon's face snake-danced before Larkin's eyes as he drew the silk slip more tightly around her throat, pulling her closer, ever closer, to him. She knew she should be concentrating on how to break his hold on her, but remembering to breathe was taking all of her effort. The simple act of drawing air into her starving lungs required more strength than she possessed.

Somewhere in the distance she heard a high-pitched wailing sound like a siren, but she couldn't focus her mind on it long enough to figure out where it came from.

All she could think about was hanging on, trying to keep afloat when going under was becoming more seductive by the second. How easy it would be to just let go, let it happen, give up....

"Let her go, Franklin!"

Gordon turned toward the man's voice in the doorway. His grip tightened and she sagged against him, gasping for breath.

"Come a step closer and I'll kill her."

"You *are* killing her," the man's voice said. "Let her go."

It was impossible to think, impossible to breathe. Her body moved on pure instinct, clawing for freedom, for air, and she bit down hard on Gordon's hand.

That was all she needed to do. In the split second it took for her lungs to gulp in great draughts of air, Alex sprang across the room and knocked Gordon to the floor.

"Call the cops," Alex ordered in a voice so filled with rage that it sounded foreign to her. "Tell them to move their asses before I kill him."

THE ELATION HE FELT when his fist connected against Gordon's jaw sent adrenaline sizzling through his body like electricity seeking ground. He was alive with rage; the primitive urge to defend a mate overpowered whatever logic he had left. He'd lost Rikki to something he couldn't fight against; he'd go to hell and back to make sure he didn't lose Larkin.

For one terrifying, exhilarating moment Alex Jakobs was capable of murder.

Dimly he heard Larkin's voice on the telephone, and he realized that she was unharmed—scared, yes, but alive. Thank God, she was alive.

The young man trembled beneath his hands. The smell of sweat and fear clung to his skin and flooded Alex's nostrils. Franklin looked pathetically young; his eyes were too big for his narrow face, and tears slid over his temples and disappeared into his hairline.

"Alex?" Larkin was at his side. The touch of her hand on his shoulder was a balm. "They're sending a squad car right over."

Racking sobs broke from Gordon's body, rising up from a loneliness Alex understood intimately. His rage took a sharp, unexpected turn into pity—for both of them—and the professional in Alex rose to the surface again, summoned up by the sound of a person in torment.

"Does he have a doctor?" Alex asked Larkin, keeping his hand on Gordon's shoulder as the young man sobbed. "Someone we can call?"

"He's an outpatient," she said, naming a nearby psychiatric center. "Patti gave me all the information when I hired him, but I can't think straight."

"Call the hospital," Alex said, "and ask for Dr. Bosworth. Tell him the story and say we need a team here stat. This kid doesn't need the cops. He needs help."

Larkin disappeared again, and when she did, Gordon's crying slowed down.

"I don't need your pity," he spat at Alex. "I don't want your help."

"That's fine," Alex said, "but you're getting it, anyway."

Gordon looked away from him, and in his face Alex saw the direction his own life might have taken. Life hadn't played fair with either one of them, but love had turned Alex's life around. Rikki's love had made it possible for him to expand his horizons and not grow suspicious and solitary as Gordon had.

Tonight he had made the final break with his past and come full circle. He loved Larkin—that fact was undeniable. But he wanted everything she had: her mind, her heart, her body.

The stakes were too high and he wasn't willing to settle for anything less.

THEY COULDN'T FIND Patti anywhere. Larkin had tried Vladimir's penthouse suite at the Garden City Hotel with no luck. Ultimately it was Gordon's doctor from the psychiatric center and two attendants who took him away. The police had showed up not long after Larkin called them, but after one look at Gordon, tearful and trembling on the floor, they knew it wasn't a police matter at all.

It was a matter of the heart.

Now the house was empty except for Larkin and Alex.

"A hell of a Thanksgiving," Alex said, accepting a snifter of brandy from her.

She glanced at the clock by the fireplace. "Only two more minutes left, thank God. I wouldn't care to go through another day like this."

They raised glasses to each other and she took a sip of the liqueur, relishing the warmth that spread outward from her chest.

"Alex?" He turned and met her eyes. "Why did you come back here tonight?"

"To make sense out of things," he said without hesitation. "To see where we really stand. I love you too much to let it end like that."

Simple words. Profound emotion. He faced her head-on, open and vulnerable, something she had been unwilling to do until now. *Tell him, you fool. Tell him how you feel.*

This was the moment she'd been waiting for. She half expected a swell of organ music to blossom offstage. "You asked me a question earlier this evening," she said softly. "I'd like to give you my answer."

He crossed his arms over his chest and leaned against the mantel. "You gave me your answer. You said you needed time."

Didn't he know a hundred years had passed since they sat in his car at the beach?

"It just took this horror with Gordon to make me realize I've been running scared." She let her emotional armor drop. "Yes, I'll marry you, Alex Jakobs."

There was no organ music, no choir of angels and—worst of all—no answer from Alex.

FOUR HOURS AGO those words, "Yes, I'll marry you," would have catapulted Alex somewhere beyond the Milky Way. Now he needed more than words.

"Say something, Alex. This isn't the way I had it pictured." She moved over to where he stood near the fireplace. "I love you so much."

"It's not enough, Larkin." Was he really saying this? Why not take what she offered and be thankful? He'd already known more happiness in the past two months than most people knew in a lifetime.

She put her drink down on the mantel. "I love you and I want to spend my life with you. What more can I offer?"

"Everything." She stared at him. "I want all of you—no halfway measures. I don't want to lie with you at night and wonder if your heart is somewhere else."

"Rikki is a tough act to follow, Alex. If I'm willing to take a chance, why aren't you?"

"I've leveled with you about Rikki," he said carefully, "and she isn't going to show up one Thanksgiving and turn our lives inside out."

"Like Vladimir?"

"I expect you to have a past, Larkin, but when the past shows up on the doorstep, that's something else entirely."

"I don't love him, Alex. I haven't for a long time."

"I believe that, but I also know things aren't over between you."

She said nothing.

"Finish it, Larkin. Whatever it is that pulls you to him, confront it, then put it behind you once and for all."

Her smile was rueful. "That's the trouble with falling in love with a shrink. Too perceptive. Too logical. You should have swept me off my feet—Alex the Blackhearted would have."

"If you can't come to me without reservation, don't come to me at all, Larkin." His control snapped and he pulled her against him in a fierce embrace. "I love you, but I'll give you up before I share you with any man." He kissed her and tasted brandy on her lips. "It's up to you."

He loved her too much to have her for a little while, only to lose her to an old love. He'd tasted loss before, and he didn't think he could bear that pain again.

"I love you, Alex," she said as they said goodbye at the door. "That will never change."

But, of course, change was the one constant in life, and Alex wondered what kind of fool would send the woman he loved back into the arms of the man she'd left.

Maybe Alex the Blackhearted had the right idea after all. Maybe a taste of paradise was better than none at all.

All he could do now was wait.

Chapter Nineteen

Vladimir Karpov's two-bedroom suite at the Garden City Hotel was one of the most expensive accommodations on Long Island.

Larkin should know. The Learning Center was footing the nine-hundred-and-fifty-dollar-per-night tab on the suite. If that didn't give her the right to bang on his door at 7:00 A.M. on the day after Thanksgiving, nothing did.

She knocked sharply three times, waited, then knocked again. From somewhere inside she heard the familiar sound of a Russian curse.

"No room service," he called out. "Not before noon."

"It's Larkin," she said, trying not to wake the rest of the guests. "I want to talk to you."

There were more muttered curses, a woman's voice, the sound of footsteps approaching. The door swung open.

"You are full of surprises, my love." He kissed her on both cheeks and ushered her inside the massive drawing room. She tried to ignore the fact that he wore a short silk robe that barely covered his buttocks. "A call, though, would have simplified things."

She looked around. "Is Patti here?"

He pushed his thick blond hair off his forehead. "A lady's privacy is paramount."

"Her brother is in the hospital. He needs to see her. If you'd answered the telephone last night, I wouldn't have to break it to her like this."

He disappeared into the bedroom, and minutes later a distraught and disheveled Patti Franklin appeared.

"Oh, God, Larkin," she said, as Larkin hugged her. "Was he in an accident? Is he—?"

"Nothing like that, Patti." Briefly Larkin explained what had happened, leaving out the more personal details. "My car's downstairs," she said, handing the young woman the keys. "Take it. Gordon needs you with him, Patti."

"What about you?"

"I'll call a cab." She gave her a gentle push. "Go."

Patti was gone before Vladimir finished dressing.

"Patricia is gone?"

Larkin nodded. She couldn't help noticing that Patti hadn't said goodbye to him.

Vladimir sat down on the sofa opposite Larkin and stretched his long legs out in front of him. His bare feet grazed her ankles and she moved away. "You do terrible things to my social life, my love. You owe me an apology."

"You'll survive," she said dryly. "I'm sure you have five more Patti Franklins waiting in the wings."

"Such cynicism." He reached for the phone and dialed room service. "Do you still like Mimosas and scrambled eggs?"

"Make it plain orange juice and toast."

He made a face, but placed her order as she gave it. "First you take my new lover away from my bed, then you insult me. What else brings you here before dawn?"

"Check your watch, Vladimir. It's after seven."

"So literal, my love, so businesslike. Why, then, do I think this visit is not strictly business?"

She dodged the question until room service arrived. However, as soon as the white-uniformed waiter disappeared, Vladimir, Bloody Mary in hand, was back on track.

"You did not come here just for Patricia, did you?"

"Very perceptive of you." She slowly sipped her orange juice. "We have some unfinished business." She'd been awake all night planning what she would say to Vladimir and how she would say it.

"About the workshop?"

"About us."

He leaned forward. "You are more direct." He finished his drink and put it on the table between them. "I think I like this change in you, my love."

"That's not important, Vladimir. What *is* important is the fact that I like the change in me."

He reached for a piece of dark Russian bread and tore off a chunk with his teeth. "Your Alex—does he like this independence in a woman?"

"He values independence in anyone, man or woman."

"How enlightened." He leaned back on the sofa. "Perhaps had I not been so European in outlook, you would not have left me."

"You didn't do anything I didn't allow." Amazing how clear things suddenly seemed. Vladimir had required constant attention, constant tending. She had willingly adopted a posture of servitude, and he couldn't be blamed totally for taking advantage of it. "It took me three years to realize the fault was as much mine as yours."

The perennial twinkle in his blue eyes disappeared. For the first time since she'd known him, Vladimir Karpov looked his age.

"I think of you often these years, my love. I—"

She laughed out loud. "You never thought of me when I slept next to you every night. Why think of me now?"

"Because, strange to tell, I miss you still."

"You don't miss me, Vladimir. You just find it difficult to accept the fact that one got away." She smiled at him. "I consider that my one claim to fame."

He didn't laugh with her. Something inside her heart softened toward him.

"I make things hard on you." Under stress, he reverted to the present tense. "I take and take, and what do I give?" His large, slender hands fanned out in a graceful gesture of defeat. "Nothing. I give nothing."

"And I asked for nothing. We made a perfect couple."

He offered her a piece of sausage, but she shook her head.

"For months I'd planned how I would dazzle you with my business acumen and astound you with my sophistication. I wanted you to marvel at my success and wonder how you ever let such a treasure get away."

"But I show up at your house and ruin everything?"

"Exactly. There I was, your little bourgeois darling, with her family and friends, doing the same things I was doing when I left you. What had changed?"

He said nothing.

"Well, I finally figured it out: *I* had changed, Vladimir. It didn't matter whether you saw me at home or at the Center. I like my life and I like the woman I've become." She no longer cared if he was impressed by her success; the fact that she had succeeded was reward enough.

"American women care so much for these things. In Europe life is simpler." The twinkle in his eye returned. "In Europe, man is king—much better system."

She laughed and tossed her linen napkin at him. "You're still impossible. It's nice to know some things never change." She stood up.

He stood up also and took her hands in his. "We make mistakes along the way, you and I. We see life differently. I wish change is possible."

Years ago that simple statement would have sent her spirits skyward with hope. Now it didn't matter. She knew exactly what she wanted out of life.

"Don't ever change, Vladimir," she said lightly. "You'd disappoint so many women if you did."

"For you, perhaps I try."

"You're a gallant liar. Thank you."

"I see you at the big dinner Sunday night?"

"Of course. I'm looking forward to it."

She quickly ran over some of the details concerning the gala and promised to contact his manager, Mikhail, to firm up time and place. Then she looked up at Vladimir and kissed him.

No magic. No fireworks. A bittersweet longing for simpler times tugged at her heart for a moment, then disappeared. She was free at last to move forward.

Before she left, she turned back to him. "You be good to Patti, Vladimir. Don't go promising her love eternal."

He laughed and his old charm returned. "I never make promises like that, my love. I'll just leave her with happy memories."

That's not enough, Larkin thought as the elevator glided back down to the lobby. She wanted a hell of a lot more than memories to warm her in her old age.

She wanted Alex Jakobs and she wasn't going to take no for an answer.

SLEEP WAS IMPOSSIBLE. Movement was the only answer.

By 9:00 A.M., Alex had run three miles, washed and waxed his car, repaired the back fence on his property, then driven out to the airport. He'd exhausted all of his earth-bound activities and was going to take to the air in an attempt to keep one step ahead of his thoughts.

Only a wise man or a fool would have encouraged the woman he loved to confront her past, and at the moment, Alex had a pretty good idea which term best suited him. He should have taken a lesson from his Halloween alter ego, Alex the Blackhearted, and thrown Larkin over his shoulder and spirited her away.

He was still chuckling over the image of himself in thigh-high boots striding off down Jericho Turnpike when he stepped inside the office of the control tower to file his flight plan.

"You're early today, Alex," the ground coordinator said. "Going somewhere special?"

"Any place but here. How does Newport sound?" He tried not to think about the plans he'd once had concerning Larkin and Newport and a ring he'd spotted in a jewelry store in the center of town.

The coordinator punched a couple of buttons on his computer terminal. The printer clicked on. "Some fog, but it's still okay." He handed Alex a weather and traffic report and a current sectional chart. "Hang loose."

Alex took the printout from Gene, then jogged back to his Cessna. He was finishing his preflight check when he heard the crunch of footsteps on gravel behind him. "Don't tell me, Gene! Newport's socked in, and the only place left on the Eastern Seaboard is Philadelphia."

He turned. Larkin, looking tired and anxious and absolutely beautiful, stood twenty feet away.

"If I were Philadelphia, I'd be furious," she said, walking toward him. "You should have more respect for the Cradle of Liberty. Think of our forefathers slaving over the Declaration of Independence, struggling with—"

"My apologies to Philadelphia," he said, struggling to sound as if his whole future didn't rest in her hands. "I'll send the chamber of commerce a donation."

She stopped in front of him. The early sunlight sparkled in the pale highlights of her amber hair.

"I finally found Patti."

It was a good thing that she spoke first; he was having trouble forming a coherent sentence. "I'm glad," he managed at last. "How did she take the news?"

"She's upset, but she's a survivor. She's with Gordon now."

He leaned against the open door of his Cessna. "Where did you finally track her down?"

"The Garden City Hotel. Penthouse suite."

His stomach clenched. "With Karpov?"

Larkin nodded. "Afraid I put quite a damper on their morning frolic."

He couldn't muster any sympathy for the Russian. "He'll live."

"No doubt." Larkin's eyes twinkled. He didn't want to speculate what that meant.

He looked toward the small parking lot beyond the chain-link fence. "Where's your car?" There was no sign of her red Datsun anywhere.

"Patti has it."

"How did you get here?"

"Taxi."

"Must have cost a fortune." *Good going, Jakobs. Woo her with witty conversation.*

"It did." She moved closer to him. "First I went to your house, then your office. This was my last resort—I'm almost out of money."

"Good timing. I'm cleared for takeoff in ten minutes."

"Then I'll get right to the point." Her eyes never left his. He hoped that was a good sign, but he was beyond rational thought. "As Roger said to me last night, 'It ain't over till it's over.'" She smiled at him. "It's over."

His heart went crazy inside his chest with hope. "You're sure?"

"I'm sure. The memories were there, but that's all." Her expression was both rueful and bemused. "I put him up in a nine-hundred-and-fifty-dollar-per-night suite to impress him and found out his opinion doesn't matter to me anymore. Ironic, isn't it?"

Not ironic, he thought. *Wonderful.*

"The memories were there, but I've found I need more than memories to warm me when I'm old and gray."

He put his flight log down on the wing of the Cessna and drew her into his arms. "Spell it out, Larkin," he said over the roar of a private jet streaking down the runway. "Where do we go from here?"

She peeked over his shoulder and checked his log. "Newport?" Her smile reached all the way to his heart. "If you could use a good navigator, I'm willing to sign on."

"It's a long trip," he said. "The ride can get pretty bumpy."

"I know. That doesn't scare me."

"I want forever from you," he said, searching her face for any lingering doubt. "I want forever or nothing at all."

She brushed his hair from his eyes, and he felt the rapid beating of her heart against his chest. "I'll give you sixty years," she said, laughing. "Then we'll renegotiate the contract."

"Sorry." He kissed her in a way that would do Alex the Blackhearted proud. "We're signing up for life."

"No escape clauses?"

He pulled her closer. "No escape clauses, no options, no renegotiations."

"You drive a hard bargain."

"The stakes are high. I want you to know what you're getting into."

"What happened to the logical Dr. Jakobs?"

"When it comes to you, I think only with my heart."

She touched his mouth with her fingertip. "I love you, Alex," she whispered. "I always will."

He opened the door of the Cessna and helped her inside.

"Why are we going to Newport?" she asked as he climbed in beside her. "A good navigator needs to know these things."

He grinned as he put on the headphones. "I know a terrific little store where we can get a jump on our Christmas shopping."

"We haven't finished the leftover turkey yet, and you're talking Christmas shopping." She shook her head and he laughed. "Sometimes you baffle me, Doctor."

Sometimes he baffled himself. Cool, logical Alex Jakobs didn't stand a chance before the power of love.

First stop was that little jewelry store in the center of town. Then, if the lady was willing, he knew of a colonial inn not too far from there that catered to newlyweds.

It would make one hell of an early Christmas present— and a great story to tell their grandchildren one day.